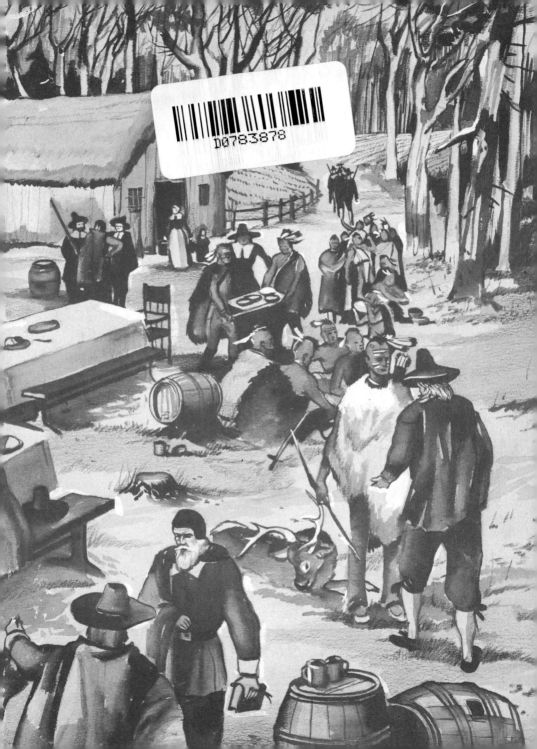

Children of the Mayflower

CHILDREN
OF THE MAYFLOWER

Mildred Houghton Comfort

Pictures by

Charles J. Peitz

Beckley-Cardy Company • Chicago

For

Ida Birdell Dewar

Contents

APPENDIX

The Good Ship Mayflower

The passengers crowded near the rail as the *Mayflower* sailed out of Plymouth Harbor. They could no longer see the faces of their friends, who were waving good-by to them from the land. The English shore seemed to grow smaller and smaller until it was out of sight. The people on the ship could see nothing but ocean.

The passengers on the *Mayflower* were the Pilgrims. They were traveling to a strange new world, where there would be no cities, streets, or houses. Their only neighbors would be savage Indians.

1

The Pilgrims felt sad to leave their friends and their homes, but they were not afraid. In the new land, America, they would be free to worship God in their own way. They would build their own colony and make their own laws.

There were more than thirty boys and girls among the passengers of the *Mayflower*. Some were only babies, and some were almost grown. Most of the children were happy and excited as the ship sailed out of Plymouth Harbor.

They could not understand why their parents seemed so sad. The new land must be an exciting place. And meanwhile, it was fun to be on a ship.

Humility Cooper and Henery Samson stood at the rail beside their cousin, Mistress Anne Tilley. The Tilleys were bringing their little cousins with them to the New World. The children were so eager to explore the ship that they could not stand still. They tugged at Mistress Tilley's wide skirt.

"Go," Mistress Tilley told them at last. "Go and look about the boat. But no mischief, mind you!"

Henery and Humility ran toward the forward part of the ship.

"The *Mayflower* is going to be our home for a long time," Humility cried joyfully.

"It's our whole country!" Henery shouted. "The decks are our streets, and the masts are our trees!"

The *Mayflower* was a good ship, strong and chunky. It had to be strong to carry its hundred and two passengers and their supplies. Every corner was packed tight. The passengers would sleep all over the ship, even in the hold.

The Pilgrims had brought chickens, goats, and pigs with them. These animals were now in pens on the forward deck. As Humility and Henery came up to the pens, they saw four children standing there—three boys and a girl. The children looked very small and lonely. The little girl was reaching through the bars to pet a rabbit. The biggest boy was stroking a goat.

"You won't butt me, will you?" he was asking.

Henery had seen these children before, but he had never spoken to them. Now he wanted to know them.

"Are you all of the same family?" he asked politely.

"Yes," answered the biggest boy. "My name is Richard More. This is my sister, Ellen, and these are my brothers. We are orphans."

"But who will take care of you?" Humility asked anxiously. "You are young to be traveling alone."

"Our masters will take care of us," Richard said. "We are bound children. We must serve our masters for seven years.

4

Ellen is with the Winslows, and Jasper is with the Carvers. This little one and I are to serve Master Brewster."

"He is a very kind man," Humility told Richard. "And you will like Mistress Brewster and the two boys, Love and Wrestling."

Humility had seen bound children before. She knew they had to work hard, but all the Pilgrim children had to work hard.

"Come on, Richard," Henery said. "Let's

go and see the shallop. We'll leave the girls here with your little brothers."

"What's a shallop?" Richard asked.

"You'll see," Henery told him.

The boys went below. Under the spar deck was a long, wide sailboat. Several children were crowding around it.

"This is the shallop, Richard," said Henery. "Isn't it a fine boat?"

The shallop looked very large.

"How many men do you think could sit in it?" asked Bartholomew Allerton, a boy about Henery's age.

"Oh, at least twenty," said Henery. "Maybe more. Maybe fifty. Maybe sixty." The shallop seemed to grow larger as he looked at it.

"A boat within a boat!" cried Richard. "A sailboat within a sailboat!"

Henery and Humility soon knew all of the children on the *Mayflower* by name. Many were old friends. There was their cousin, Elizabeth Tilley. She was fourteen years old and considered herself too grown-up to play with younger children. Then there were the Allertons—Bartholomew and his younger sister, Remember. The Brewster boys, Love and Wrestling, were also old friends of Henery's.

There were many new children, too, and Henery and Humility soon came to know them well. Giles Hopkins was thirteen, and his sister Constance was fifteen.

Henery liked to be with Giles, for the older boy seemed to know a great deal about everything. Mary Chilton was another favorite of Henery's. She was fifteen, but she often joined in the games of the younger boys and girls.

Then there were the Billington boys, Francis and John. Henery did not like them as well as he liked Giles. Francis was always getting himself and the other children into trouble.

The clothes of the children were very
much like those of their parents. The boys
had long doublets, or jackets, that reached
half way to their knees. The girls were
dressed in long, full skirts and tight basques
or waists. They wore stiff white caps.

The children's clothes were dyed brown
or green, like the brown of dry maple
leaves and the green of pine needles. Most
of the Pilgrims wore dark colors. Dark
clothes meant less washing.

The wind billowed the sails and sang in

the rigging as the *Mayflower* sailed on—westward, always westward. In good weather, the children played on deck. The air was smelly and close in the cabins. Many of the passengers were seasick. But the children stayed well. They romped over the ship, trying to help the crew and often getting in the way.

Henery liked most to feed the animals. He and Humility made friends with John Goodman's two dogs. The great mastiff and the little spaniel were the only dogs on board. Master Goodman sometimes let Henery take the spaniel for a walk on deck.

The older people talked among themselves. The children listened and then chattered eagerly to one another about what they had heard.

Giles Hopkins said that his father had been in America once years ago.

"My father says that America is a fine, rich country," Giles told Henery.

"Wasn't your father afraid of the Indians?" Henery asked.

"My father isn't afraid of anyone," Giles answered. "Besides, some of the Indians are friendly. They have known white men who have come on ships to fish and trade."

"But aren't there any English people who live where we are going?" asked Henery.

"No," Giles said. "There are English people in Virginia. But we shall have our own colony."

Henery told Giles about Holland, where children wore wooden shoes. Henery had lived in Holland with the Tilleys. Many of the passengers of the *Mayflower* had left England several years before. They had gone to Holland to live, because the Dutch people let them worship God in their own way. In England the law said that everyone had to belong to the state church.

But Holland had been crowded. It was hard to make a living there. And the Pilgrims wanted their children to grow up to be English. So the Pilgrims had decided to move again. They bought a ship, called the *Speedwell*, and went back to England. There they met another group of people, who planned to sail to America on the *Mayflower*. Some merchants in London loaned the Pilgrims the money for the trip.

The two ships had set sail together early in the summer. But the *Speedwell* leaked badly, and both ships turned back. Some of the Pilgrims on the *Speedwell* stayed in England, and some crowded themselves and their supplies into the *Mayflower*. In September the *Mayflower* made its second start for the New World.

Though it was still early in the fall, the North Atlantic wind blew free and cold. The children were warmly dressed, but they felt its bite.

Sometimes there was hot porridge for breakfast. The ship's cook prepared it in a three-legged or tripod kettle. The kettle was set over a box filled with sand, and a fire was built in the box. On fine days the cook brought this hearth box up on deck. The children liked to watch him work.

Very little cooking was done on board the *Mayflower*. The Pilgrims had enough food, but it was simple. They ate bread, dried fish, and cheese. No fruit or vegetables had been brought along.

Great barrels of water were stowed away in the hold. A young man named John Alden watched over the barrels and made sure that the water stayed fresh, for it had to last during the whole trip. John was a cooper, or barrelmaker.

Humility and Henery liked to talk to John, who was tall, blond, and friendly. Humility noticed that John often talked and walked with Priscilla Mullins. The children loved Priscilla for her pleasant smile and merry laugh.

12

Sometimes Humility walked along the deck with John and Priscilla. John liked to tease Humility because she had to trot to keep up with his long stride.

Henery would often follow Captain Miles Standish and beg him for stories of his adventures. The captain had fought in the Spanish wars when he was a young man. He had been hired by the Pilgrims to come with them and command their army. He was a short man with red hair. He was very stern, but the children liked him.

The captain grumbled a great deal because the *Mayflower* had been so late in starting. It might be December before the ship reached America.

"December? Fiddlesticks!" the women said. But the men looked very serious.

On fine days the children played shovelboard. They pushed small pieces of wood about the deck with sticks and brooms.

One day the children grew excited and noisy as they played. Henery and Giles were playing against each other, and the other children were cheering them.

Presently little Richard More came up on deck. His master, William Brewster, had sent him. Richard said that the children must stop their game. Their noise was troubling the sick people below deck.

No one dared to disobey. The children gathered at their favorite place near the rail. They looked at the blue sky and watched the waves.

Humility sniffed the air. She wrinkled her nose. "What an interesting smell the *Mayflower* has!" she said.

"The *Mayflower* smells of the things it has carried," Richard told her. "Fish and tar and timber and turpentine. The *Mayflower* has dropped anchor in many ports."

"How do you know?" asked Henery.

"Captain Jones told me," Richard said proudly.

Richard often felt shy, but he was never lonely. The little bound boy loved to watch the sailors as they worked in the rigging during a storm. Often Captain Jones stopped to talk to him. The captain was busy, but he always had time to be kind.

September days were gone. Now it was October. A great yellow moon hung in the sky at night—the harvest moon.

One morning Captain Jones called out to Giles and Henery as they passed him.

"We're halfway across!" he shouted.

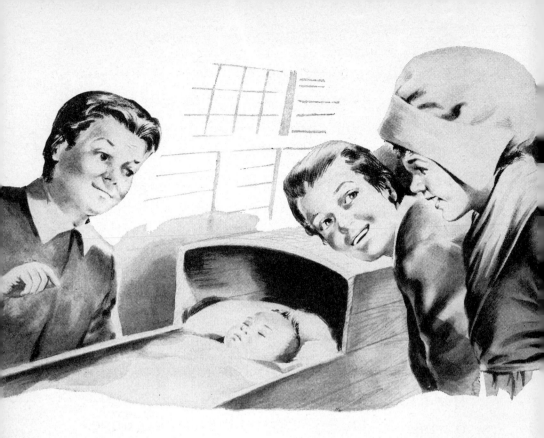

Halfway! That was wonderful news.
Giles Hopkins gave the children another
piece of exciting news. He had a new
brother—the first baby born since the
journey began.

Giles took Henery and Humility down to
see the baby. Only his tiny red face showed
in the wooden cradle.

"He seems very small," Humility said. "I think he is the tiniest baby I ever saw."

"What is his name?" asked Henery.

"Oceanus," Giles told him.

"Oceanus!" cried Henery. "What an odd name!"

"It's because Oceanus was born on the ocean," Giles explained.

"I think it's the nicest thing that could have happened on the trip," said Humility. "Oceanus! A new Pilgrim!"

Oceanus gave a loud yell, as if he himself were excited about being born on the *Mayflower*. Or it may have been simply that he was hungry.

End of the Journey

The new baby seemed to bring good luck. For some days after he was born the weather was fine. Then came November, and the storms began.

Cold waves washed over the decks of the *Mayflower*. The water leaked into the cabins. As if the waves were not wet enough, rain beat down on the ship.

One stormy day Henery and Humility heard a dreadful cry. "Man overboard!"

John Howland, the Carver servant, had gone up on deck in spite of the storm. The waves had washed him overboard But

John did not drown. He clung to a rope which was fastened to the side of the ship. The cold waves swept over him, but he held on tightly until help came.

The sailors brought a boat hook and reached down over the side of the ship. They pulled John up on deck again. He was wet and cold, but safe.

"Maybe Cousin Anne is right," Henery told Humility. "I guess we'd better stay in the cabin until the storm is over."

The wind and waves grew more fierce. The Pilgrims huddled in their cabins. They prayed for the safety of the ship.

Suddenly one night they heard a loud noise, like the shot of a cannon.

"What can it be?" they asked one another fearfully.

Captain Jones came down to talk to the passengers. The storm had broken one of the masts, he told them. There was great danger, but he hoped to repair the mast.

"God's will be done," the Pilgrims said. They had brought a great iron screw with them from Holland, thinking it might prove useful. Now the sailors used it to repair the mast.

Giles listened to them talk as they worked. "The sailors think we ought to turn back," he told Henery. "They say the ship is not safe for a long voyage."

But Captain Jones calmed the fears of the crew and the passengers. "Never fear," he said. "The *Mayflower* may leak above the water, but she is tight as can be below. We shall get there safely."

One day Captain Jones said that land could not be far away. Everyone was excited. The children stood at the rail for hours, watching the line where the sea and the sky met. They wanted to be the first ones to see the new land.

"There's a land bird!" Henery shouted, shading his eyes against the sun with his hand. He peered up at the bird. "It's not a sea gull. It's a wild duck. Captain Jones says they live along the shore."

"Look. Oh, look!" Bartholomew cried. "Down below there! There's a tree branch floating on the water!"

Even the clouds looked different. They seemed to pile up in banks, as though they were hugging a shore.

The children did not want to go to bed that night. They were too excited. After they were in their bunks, they chattered to one another.

"We will see land soon! We will see land soon!" said Humility.

"Maybe tomorrow, maybe tomorrow!" sang Henery.

"Children, children," Mistress Tilley told them. "Go to sleep. It may be days before we see land."

At daybreak the next morning, Humility and Henery were awakened by a shout.

"Land ahoy!" came the call. "Land ahoy!" A sailor had seen a dark shore line against the sky.

All the passengers dressed themselves and rushed up on deck. No one felt tired, sleepy, or ill now. Everyone was eager and excited. Soon they would reach land!

"Won't there be anyone at all to meet us?" Humility asked Mistress Tilley.

"I should hope not," Mistress Tilley said. "Who could meet us here? Only savages." Her tone made the children shiver. But they remembered what Giles had said. Some Indians were friendly.

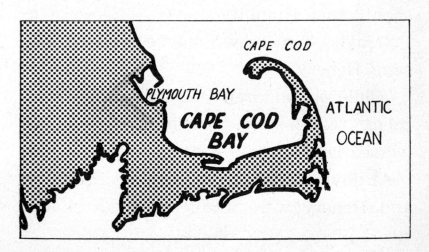

A line of low hills stood out against the sky. The sailors looked at their map. The *Mayflower* had sailed north of its course. The Pilgrims had intended to land near the mouth of the Hudson River. Instead, the ship was close to Cape Cod.

This cape was a hook of land that stuck out from the coast of Massachusetts. It had been named Cape Cod by explorers who saw many codfish near by.

The Pilgrims decided to turn southward. Until noon, the ship ran along the shore of Cape Cod. Then the *Mayflower* struck rough water.

"This place is too dangerous," said Captain Jones. "We cannot go on. We shall have to go north again."

The *Mayflower* turned and headed back up Cape Cod. By the time the ship reached calmer waters, it was too dark to go farther. The Pilgrims spent their first night in America at anchor in the open sea.

No one slept much that night. The passengers were on deck again as soon as it was light. A few hours later, the *Mayflower* sailed around the hook of Cape Cod and came into a fine, wide harbor. There was a rattle of chains as the anchor went down.

"Come," said Mistress Tilley to Henery and Humility. "We must go below and pack our things." She wanted to give the children something to do. They were so excited that they could hardly speak.

When Henery and Humility came back on deck they found that the sailors were ready to launch the longboat, a large rowboat which belonged to the ship.

"Are we going ashore?" Henery asked.

"No," said one of the sailors. "Not you, my lad, but others."

"Why don't they come, then?" another sailor asked impatiently. "Don't these men who have crossed the ocean want to see what the new land is like?"

Captain Jones came up. "Never mind, men," he told the sailors. "The landing party is not going ashore yet. The men are holding a meeting in the main cabin."

A meeting! What could be the matter? Why should there be trouble on this happy day, with land in plain sight? Henery and Humility looked at each other, and then they went to the main cabin. The door was closed, but Giles Hopkins and Richard More were standing outside it, talking earnestly.

"What is the matter?" Henery asked. "Is it a mutiny, Giles?" His eyes opened wide. He had heard stories about mutinies on shipboard.

"No," Giles said. "It is not mutiny. But there are those among us who would be their own masters, once we reach land. My father says this cannot be. We cannot all do as we please. We must work together for the good of all."

"My master is very angry," Richard said.

"What are they doing?" asked Humility.

"The men are writing a compact," Giles told her. "Everyone will sign it—all the men, I mean."

The other children did not know what a compact was, so Giles explained. A compact was an agreement, he said. When people signed it, they were making a promise. They were promising to work together and to obey the laws of the colony.

"The men are leaving the cabin!" cried Humility.

The door opened. The children watched as, one by one, the men came out. Their faces were very serious.

The children ran to the door of the cabin. The scribe still sat there, with his quill pen in his hand. He laid the quill down to sprinkle sand over the paper so that the ink would dry quickly. Then he looked up.

Humility ran away. But the three boys stayed where they were.

"Come in, my lads," the scribe said solemnly. "This is for you and for all who come after you."

The scribe pointed to the page with his quill pen. Then he read the words aloud.

"Equal laws for the general good of the colony," he said.

"Equal laws for everyone?" Giles asked.

"For everyone," said the scribe.

"Servants? Bound boys? Bound girls?" Richard asked timidly.

"For all," the scribe answered, in a deep tone. "Within their rights," he added.

The scribe told the boys that the men had agreed on a government for the new colony. They had chosen Master John Carver as their first governor. Everyone had voted for him, for he was kind and wise.

When the boys came back on deck, they found the passengers gathered there again. Everyone was looking toward the land.

The shore looked as if no one had ever lived there. The children almost wished that a few Indians were waiting for them.

The people on deck watched the first landing party go ashore. The sixteen men were rowed to the land in the longboat. They came back a few hours later. They had found sand and soil on Cape Cod, but no fresh water.

The next day was the Sabbath. The

Pilgrims spent the whole day in prayer on board ship. With all their hearts they gave thanks for their safe arrival in the New World. They asked God to help them and guide them in building their colony.

On Monday it was the women's turn to go ashore. They wanted to wash their clothes and bedding. Everything they had brought with them needed washing.

"Please take us with you," Humility and Henery begged, as the kettles and tubs for washing were loaded into the boat.

But Mistress Tilley told them they would have to stay on the ship for the present. "Wait until we are sure there are no redskins about," she said.

The women were taken ashore in the longboat. They built fires on the shore and heated ocean water for washing. Then they hung the clean clothes on bushes to dry.

While the women were washing, the longboat went back to the ship for some of the

men. The women would return to the boat
that same day, but the men planned to stay
on Cape Cod for several days.

Humility and Henery stood at the rail
and watched the sixteen men get into the
longboat. The men wore armor and carried muskets. The leaders of the party
were Captain Standish, Master William
Bradford, and Giles's father, Master
Stephen Hopkins.

Henery thought the little captain looked

very warlike. The bright sun shone on his armor and made it gleam like gold.

The children watched the longboat land and turn back toward the *Mayflower*. The dark trees quickly hid the men from sight.

A few days later, Giles and Henery were eating their porridge on deck. It was a fine, clear morning.

Suddenly Henery cried, "Look, there's smoke! Maybe some Indians are cooking their breakfast!"

Giles was excited. "No," he said, "it's a signal. It means that the men have now reached the other side of Cape Cod."

The next day the children heard a shot. Giles said that this shot was also a signal. The explorers had returned.

That night the children listened eagerly to the tale the explorers told. The first afternoon the men had seen some Indians. They followed the savages for miles, but could not catch up with them.

"The next day," said Captain Standish, "we came to a clearing. We saw mounds of sand which people had made."

The explorers dug into the mounds. They found several baskets full of corn.

The men had brought back as much corn as their pockets would hold.

"It is seed corn," said Master Hopkins. "We can use it to plant next year's crop."

The children were eager to go ashore themselves. "They saw deer!" cried Giles. "And found good water."

"The water tasted as good as anything we did ever drink," said Master Bradford. "But we fear that this Cape Cod is no fit place for our colony. There is not enough water, and no open land for farms."

"We shall have to be patient," said Governor Carver. "Let us pray for God's help. He will guide us to our new home."

The Long Landing

Only two weeks later Giles and Henery watched a group of men set out on another exploring trip. This time twenty-four of the men were going. They were sailing in the shallop, which was ready at last. They planned to stay away as long as possible and to bring back all the corn they could.

"I don't see why Father wouldn't let me go along," Giles told Henery. "I am almost grown now and could have helped."

"I don't see why, either," Henery said loyally. It seemed to him there was nothing Giles could not do.

"I guess he wanted me to stay here to protect Mother and the children," Giles said slowly. "Mother will feel safer with me on board."

Soon after the men had left, it began to snow. Great feathery flakes fell all day from a gray sky. Nor did the snow stop as darkness came.

That night another little boy was born. His name was Peregrine White.

"He looks just as Oceanus did," Humility remarked to Mary Chilton. Peregrine was small, red, and helpless, but his voice was loud. He seemed to be protesting against the world to which he had come.

When Henery and Giles went back on deck, they found work for them to do. A white carpet of snow lay over the deck. The boys were told to shovel it off.

"I wonder how the men are getting along," said Giles. "This snow will make it hard for them to find the Indian mounds."

The men returned in the shallop several days later. Some of them were ill, and all were cold. But they had a great tale to tell. Indians had attacked them as they camped on shore, and they had driven the Indians away with their musket fire.

Henery and Giles helped carry baskets and bags to the main cabin. The women came to see what the men had brought.

There were ten bushels of corn and some beans. It was exciting to watch the Indian treasure being unloaded. All the children crowded inside the cabin. The women touched the beautiful Indian baskets.

"It seems impossible," Mistress Hopkins said to Mistress Tilley. "How could savages make such lovely baskets?"

Giles noticed that Richard looked very worried. Giles thought that he was anxious about his brother Jasper, who was ill.

But Richard was not thinking about his brother now. He had another worry. He knew it was wrong to take things that belonged to other people. Yet—the Pilgrims had robbed the Indians of their supplies and their treasures.

"Won't the Indians need the corn?" Everyone heard Richard's timid voice.

Governor Carver answered Richard very seriously. "You see, Richard," he told the little boy, "we could not find any Indians to pay them for the corn. But we shall

pay them when we meet them. Meanwhile, our need for the corn is very great. We shall plant it next spring. You know that we must have food, or we shall not live."

Then the governor turned to Master Brewster. "The child is old for his years," Governor Carver said. "He takes our cares on his shoulders."

Francis Billington was a different sort of child. Nothing bothered him. Someone was always cuffing him, until it seemed a wonder his ears were not out of shape.

One day Francis almost fell overboard as he ran and slid on the slippery deck. He would have fallen into the deep, cold water if Giles had not caught him.

Henery and Giles very often grew tired of Francis' teasing. One afternoon they turned their backs on him. Henery was glad when Francis went below deck.

Suddenly a booming roar shook the whole ship. A gun had gone off.

Women screamed and men shouted. The Pilgrims rushed into the Billington cabin. There stood Francis—safe, but frightened. He had shot off his father's musket, right inside the cabin.

One of the sailors pointed to an open keg of gunpowder which stood close by.

Francis grew white and trembled. He knew that he had done a dreadful thing. He might easily have blown up the *Mayflower* and all its passengers.

When his father punished him, Francis did not cry. He took his beating like a man. But later he sobbed as he sat by himself in a corner. "It was all their fault," he said to himself. "If they had been nicer to me, I would have stayed on deck."

These were days of sorrow for many of the passengers of the *Mayflower*. Jasper More died, and then James Chilton, Mary's father. Many people were ill.

"God's will be done," said the Pilgrims.

The men made several more exploring trips. Finally they chose a place for their colony. This place was west of Cape Cod, on Plymouth Bay.

The Indians had cleared fields on this shore, and then they had gone away. The place seemed to be the best the Pilgrims could find. Besides, the weather was growing colder.

Master Christopher Jones, the captain of the *Mayflower*, wanted to go back to England. He had promised to stay as long as the Pilgrims needed him and his ship. But they had been in the New World for more than a month now.

The Pilgrims decided to build their settlement near a little river which emptied into Plymouth Bay. They named this stream Jones River, in honor of the captain.

A few days before Christmas, all the men went ashore, ready to build their colony on the Jones River.

The men began to cut wood for building. But a storm came, and they had to go back to the ship. It was several days before the weather cleared enough so that a group could come ashore again.

Christmas Day was just a day of hard work to the Pilgrims. On this first Christmas in America, there were no merry bells. Only the buzz of saws and the crack of axes could be heard.

Giles went ashore with the men on Christmas day, but Henery stayed on the ship with Humility and the other children. The women were very busy. They prepared meals and cared for the sick people.

Out in the clearing the men were building a large house. They worked from dawn to dusk, and often far into the night. The frame of the house was twenty feet square. The sides were made of rough boards.

The children watched as first the walls were built, then the chimney, and finally

the roof. The roof was made of bundles of grass fastened together. It was called a thatched roof and was made very steep, so that it would shed rain or snow.

This big house was called the common house. Here, after the town was built, the people could meet together. About half the Pilgrims were to live in this house while more houses were being built. The others would stay on the *Mayflower* for a time.

The men built a lean-to, or shed, against the common house. In it the Pilgrims would keep their tools and supplies.

"We'll all live in one house," Humility

said, "except the people who stay on the ship until more houses can be built. Won't it be fun?"

"Better still," Mary Chilton said, "it will be safer if Indians should attack us."

Every night the workmen came back to the *Mayflower* to sleep. The bay was not deep enough to anchor the ship close to shore, so the men went back and forth in the longboat. Each night several men stayed on shore to guard the house.

In the evenings, the Pilgrims planned their town. They were building their houses between the river and the bay. On one side of the little settlement was a hill. The Pilgrims would place their cannon there. Then they could guard the low fields to the north.

One night, John Goodman and Peter Browne did not return to the *Mayflower*. It was two days before they limped into the clearing, half-frozen. They said that they had been lost. They had wandered off into the woods, taking the dogs with them. When they turned to come back, they found they did not know which way to go.

Another night, the people on the ship saw a red glow. The thatched roof of the big house had caught fire from a spark. The men on shore managed to put out the blaze. They had to put a new roof on the house.

The men began to bring their supplies over from the ship. It was easy to move the bedding, the clothes, and the few pieces of furniture. But carrying the great hogsheads of meal was heavy work. All the carrying and rowing made the Pilgrims long for the time when this part of their task would be done.

Each family was supposed to build its own cottage. So many were sick, however, that the work went very slowly. The cottages, like the common house, were built of boards, twigs, and clay.

One little house was the hospital. Here the Pilgrims faithfully tended their sick people. Nearly half the passengers of the *Mayflower* died of hunger and sickness during that first dreadful winter.

Captain Jones was always kind. One day he brought five geese and some venison, or deer meat. He said the food was to be cooked for the sick people. The Pilgrims were all very grateful to him.

As they worked, the Pilgrims began to see Indians. They were always far away. One day Captain Standish and Francis Cooke left some tools in the woods. When they went back, the tools had disappeared. Some Indians had carried them off.

The Pilgrims hurried to bring their cannons ashore. They placed them on platforms at the top of the hill—Fort Hill, they called it later. Now that the big guns were ready, the women felt safer.

One day in early March, the children

were sent to pick up dry sticks for kindling. The day was sunny and pleasant,
and Henery and Humility went farther
into the woods than they meant to. Suddenly they looked up to see an Indian
coming toward them. He walked along
with a strong, free stride, and his mus-
cular brown body seemed to shine in
the sunlight.

The children ran home. Outside the common house they met Captain Standish. They told him about the Indian. The captain looked fierce and warlike, and he prepared his gun for action.

To everyone's surprise, the Indian smiled as he came to meet the Pilgrims. They were even more surprised when he spoke an English word.

"Welcome," he said.

Humility and Henery were so happy that they felt like jumping up and down. It was wonderful to be in a strange land and to be made welcome by one who dwelt there.

The Good Welcome

The Pilgrims stopped the Indian just as he was about to enter the common house. As they talked to him, they could not help staring at him and his large bow and arrow.

The Indian explained that he had seen their ship and had thought it was stopping in the harbor during a fishing trip. White men's ships often came to this coast for fishing. The Indian lived about a day's sail away, on an island called Monhegan.

"How does it happen that you speak English?" asked the Pilgrims.

He had learned a few words of English,

the Indian said, from sailors who had stopped farther up the coast.

The Pilgrims brought the Indian into the common house. They threw a horseman's red coat around his shoulders, for the wind was chilly. The Indian was not at all cold, but he liked the color of the coat. The women brought him biscuits and butter, with cheese and a piece of duck.

The Indian ate hungrily and seemed to enjoy every bite. He also seemed to like all the attention he was getting.

The children crowded around him, and he smiled at them. Then he asked their names, and told them his name—Samoset. This was a name they would never forget— Samoset, their first Indian friend.

Governor Carver asked Samoset why the Indians did not use Plymouth Harbor. He also wanted to know why the Indians had left their cornfields. Why were there no wigwams in the clearing where the new houses were going up? Surely Indians had lived there once.

"Many Indians once live here," Samoset explained. "Fine tribe—many, many braves. Patuxet live here. But many moons ago— four years, you English say—great sickness come. Patuxet all die."

"They died?" Henery, standing at the Indian's elbow, could hardly believe this sad story. "Every one?"

Samoset nodded solemnly. "Every one," he said.

The Indian went on to tell them that the name Patuxet meant Little Bay or Little Falls. Had the Englishmen come a few years earlier, Samoset said, they might have found it hard to make a landing here.

Samoset made himself quite at home. He seemed to have no intention of leaving. The Pilgrims were a little worried. They did not know what he might do next.

"Samoset may lodge in Master Hopkins'

house," Governor Carver decided. The Hopkins house was almost finished. "Someone shall watch him," the governor added.

Henery and Humility thought that Giles was very lucky to have Samoset stay in his house. The children felt no doubts at all about Samoset. They trusted him at once, and he told them many things. He belonged to the tribe of the Wampanoag, he said. His chief, whose name was Massasoit, or Yellow Feather, ruled the Indians in this part of the country.

Now Samoset had questions of his own to ask. Why didn't the Pilgrims build wigwams? Why did the women stay inside while the men did the heavy work? Mary Chilton explained that the women had their own work to do. They washed, cleaned, cooked, and cared for their babies. They also made the family clothing.

As for wigwams—well, wigwams were not strong enough, and they were smoky. It was not easy for Mary to explain to Samoset that the white man had his own way of living.

Samoset kept shaking his head as he watched the men plastering clay on their walls of rough boards. Most of all he marveled at the careful way they built their chimneys and fireplaces. Why should the white people mind a little smoke in their wigwams? The Indians didn't. They built their fires on the floor and let the smoke go up through openings in the roof.

The Pilgrims had gifts ready for Samoset when he left the next morning. They gave him a knife, a bracelet, and a ring. Governor Carver told him to be sure to come back as soon as he had beaver skins or other furs he wanted to trade.

The next day was Sunday. The Pilgrims were ready to begin their prayer meeting when they saw Samoset coming. He had five strong young braves with him.

Samoset, of course, had no idea of the way the Pilgrims kept the Sabbath. He did not know they listened to sermons all day long. They did not even cook on Sunday, but ate cold food.

The Pilgrims were not very happy to see Samoset back so soon, and on the Sabbath, too. But they greeted the Indians in a very friendly manner.

It was plain that Samoset had praised the Pilgrims' cooking. He and his friends ate so heartily that the Pilgrims became worried. If the Indians kept visiting them, how could they make their food last through the winter?

When they had finished eating, the Indians jumped to their feet.

"Now what are they going to do?" the children asked one another.

With Samoset as their leader, the Indians began to sing and dance wildly. The children tried not to smile. Dancing was a sin, and dancing on Sunday was a double sin. Of course the Indians did not know this. They were only trying to thank the Pilgrims.

The older people looked very serious, but they said nothing. Their faces grew happier when the Indians suddenly brought out the tools which had been lost.

Then the Indians offered them several beaver skins for trade. Now what would the Pilgrims do, the children wondered. It was a sin to trade on Sunday. Yet the settlers wanted and needed the beaver skins.

"We don't want to trade for just a few skins," Governor Carver told the Indians. "Besides, today is our holiday. We do not trade on Sunday. You must be sure to come back another day and bring more skins. Then we shall trade for all."

The Indians finally left, taking their beaver skins with them. The Pilgrims hoped they were not offended, but they could not be sure.

Samoset came back again only a few days later. This time an Indian brave named Squanto was with him. Squanto could speak English even better than Samoset.

Squanto had once belonged to the Patuxet tribe, and had lived in this very place. English traders had kidnaped him and had taken him to London. It was years before he got back to Patuxet. He found that his whole tribe had been wiped out by illness. Squanto went to live with the Wampanoag, but now he was glad to meet the Pilgrims.

He knew white men's ways and liked them.

Squanto and Samoset had news. Their great chief, Massasoit, was close by. This news was a surprise. The Indians had moved through the woods so silently that the Pilgrims had not seen or heard them.

Now the Pilgrims looked where Samoset pointed. There, at the top of the hill, were

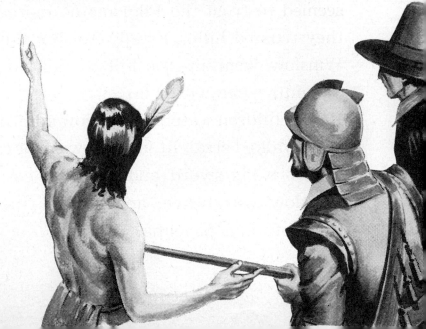

sixty Indians, with their chief. All had their faces painted brightly. The chief was tall and straight, a fine-looking man. He wore a chain of white bone beads about his neck. A long pipe hung down from it in front, and in back dangled a tobacco pouch.

Squanto told the Pilgrims that Massasoit wanted them to come up the hill for a pow-wow, or meeting. The Pilgrims refused. They wanted Massasoit to come down to them, and to leave most of his men where they were.

Massasoit did not want to do this. He seemed to trust the Pilgrims no more than they trusted him. Finally Master Edward Winslow went up the hill to talk to him. Squanto went with him.

The children watched Winslow admiringly as he walked straight into the warrior camp. He wore his sword and his steel corselet. Winslow was brave, and yet his manner was soft and pleasing.

Winslow greeted the Indian chief very politely and made a graceful speech. Squanto repeated the speech in the Indian language. Massasoit liked the speech, and he liked Winslow's sword and corselet even better. He told Winslow he would like to trade for them.

Winslow changed the subject. He invited the Indian chief to visit the Pilgrims.

"If you will, bring a few of your braves with you," Winslow said. "I myself will show that you are welcome by staying here while you are gone. Then your men may be sure that no harm will come to you."

Massasoit accepted the invitation. He marched down the hill with several of his braves. Captain Standish met him at the edge of town and led him down the street. The captain had a group of his soldiers with him. The men wore armor and carried their guns. They looked very warlike.

The women and children crowded around

as the captain led the chief through the town. Massasoit was three or four heads taller than Standish, but the little captain showed no fear. He strutted along in a very dignified manner. Giles and Henery felt proud of him.

The Pilgrims led Massasoit to a house that was nearly finished. To make the place look better, they had brought in a green rug and some bright cushions. As the chief sat down on the cushions, there was a sudden beating of drums and a blare of trumpets. Governor Carver stood in the doorway. Behind him was another company of armed men. The governor stopped at the door for a moment, and bowed to the Indian chief. Then he came in and sat down on a cushion, too.

The Pilgrims were as solemn as possible, so that the Indians would take the meeting very seriously. Carver and Massasoit each made a speech. Squanto repeated Carver's speech in the Indian language and Massasoit's speech in the English language. Then Massasoit and the Pilgrims promised each other a lasting friendship. And they made a peace treaty.

The treaty was written down. The words were simple. Both the Pilgrims and the Indians understood it, and both meant to keep the promises in it. They pledged "to do no hurt" to one another, in any way. If an Indian did wrong and broke the peace, he was to be sent to Plymouth. If a Pilgrim broke the peace, he must be sent to Sowams, where Massasoit lived. The guilty ones would be punished.

Indians who came to Plymouth must leave their weapons behind. Pilgrims who went to visit the Indians must leave their guns behind. If an enemy attacked the Pilgrims, the Indians were to help. The Pilgrims promised to help if an enemy attacked the Indians.

The treaty was to include all the tribes of the Wampanoag.

It was a great moment in Plymouth when Massasoit made his mark on the treaty paper. Then Governor Carver signed his name. Both men hoped for peace. But neither the governor nor the chief knew that this treaty would last forty years— until the death of Massasoit.

Carver went with Massasoit as far as the

town brook. Behind them came Standish
and his little army. The drums beat loudly,
and the trumpets played. It was a real
parade. At the brook, Massasoit and Carver
stopped to say good-by. There were more
speeches.

But Squanto did not want to say good-by.
He wanted to stay in Plymouth with the

Pilgrims. Here his people had lived and died, and here he wanted to remain.

"Squanto help white man," the Indian told the governor.

Carver turned to Captain Miles Standish. "Shall we let him stay?" he asked.

"Yes," said the captain. "He can be very useful to us. He can go with us on trading trips and put our speech into the Indian tongue."

"Very well, Squanto," the governor told the Indian. "You may stay. You shall live with us and work with us."

When Winslow came down the hill again, he was glad to hear about the treaty.

"Now we can live in peace," Winslow said. "We have friends instead of enemies for neighbors. The Lord has been very good to us."

Mayflower Farewell

Now the Pilgrims felt safe. They had signed a peace treaty with the Indians. They no longer feared attack. But there was a new worry.

Indians began to drop in for visits. They came at any hour of the day or night, and always expected food and drink. The Pilgrims began to wonder if their stores would last the winter.

The men held a meeting. They decided to send Edward Winslow and Stephen Hopkins to see Chief Massasoit. Squanto would guide them to the Indian camp.

Master Hopkins told his family all about the trip when he came home.

"The journey was a hard one," he said. "We were very hungry by the time we got to the Indian camp.

"Squanto spoke for us. We told Massasoit that we wanted to be friends with all the Indians. Yet we did not have much food. We could not feed a great many Indians every day and still have enough for ourselves.

"Massasoit seemed to understand. It seems the Indians have to make their food go a long way, too. The chief promised to keep his braves at home. And he said his people will sell us corn and game—as much as they can spare. They will trade beaver skins for whatever we have to give them."

"Is that good, Father?" asked Giles.

"It is very good," his father told him. "We need beaver skins to pay our debt to the men in London. They let us have money for the voyage. They expect us to send fish or furs back in the *Mayflower* to repay them."

"You certainly were hungry when you came home, Father," Giles said. "You would not talk until you had eaten."

"There was no food in the Indian camp," said Giles' father. "We waited and waited, then finally the Indians gave us a small piece of fish. The chief felt ashamed that he could not offer us more. We had to come home hungry."

Spring was near. The time had come when the *Mayflower* must sail for home. The ship had stayed in the New World for almost five months. Now the Pilgrims were settled in their new homes, and Captain Jones could leave.

The ship floated on the sea, light as a water lily. The *Mayflower* had been heavily loaded on the trip over. Now it carried little more than wood for fuel and water for the return voyage. The merchants in London would be disappointed. There was nothing to send back.

The crew put rocks in the hold. The rocks would keep the ship steady on the return voyage.

The shallop was to be left behind for the Pilgrims. They planned to use it for trading trips along the coast.

As the Pilgrims went from shore to boat and back again, their faces grew very sad. Captain Jones saw the look of longing in their eyes.

"Why not come back with me?" he asked. "Think of England in the spring! I will take anyone who wants to go."

The Pilgrims did not answer at first. Finally Governor Carver said, "Anyone who wants to should feel free to go. We have had a hard time here. It would be no disgrace to return home."

"Why stay in this strange land?" cried

Captain Jones. "Why go through another terrible New England winter? Do you like to live with savages for neighbors?"

The Pilgrims did not argue with him. But no one wanted to leave. This, they said, was where the Lord had sent them, and this was where they would stay.

"Don't you want to send some of the children back with me?" the captain asked.

But the children did not want to go. "No," they said. "We would rather stay."

"Every single one of you?" Captain Jones grumbled, but his voice sounded admiring. He could not understand why the Pilgrims wanted to stay, but he admired and loved them for their courage.

Soon afterward, the sailors loosened the *Mayflower's* sails. The ship was under way at full tide, its colors floating in the breeze. Captain Jones gave a final farewell with flags and guns. His heart was full. He had stayed with the Pilgrims as long as they

needed him. They were his friends and he would never forget them.

Captain Standish ordered a return salute from the Plymouth big guns. The whole population of the town had turned out for the occasion. Nobody stayed indoors. Even those who were sick struggled up Fort Hill to see the *Mayflower* sail. It was an important occasion for the whole colony.

Mothers carried their babies in their arms, while smaller children clung to their skirts. Some of the older children helped to take care of younger ones.

Humility and Henery had tears in their eyes as they watched the *Mayflower* get smaller and smaller. They looked around. The women were weeping and the men looked very serious.

The *Mayflower* had been a home, a shelter, and a meeting place. Its captain had been a faithful friend. Now the Pilgrims were alone in a strange world.

For once there was no hurry about getting back to work. The Pilgrims kept watching the *Mayflower* until it seemed to be only a speck in the distance.

There was little time for sadness. The Pilgrims had to plant their grain. Every man and every boy worked in the fields from sunrise until it was too dark to see.

Governor Carver worked in the fields with the others. Suddenly, one afternoon, he stumbled and put his hand to his head.

Working in the sun too long had given him a sunstroke. The governor died only a few hours later.

The Pilgrims grieved for him. The kindly, gray-bearded old man had been their leader through the hard winter that had just passed. It seemed very sad that he should die just when things looked better.

"What will we do, Father?" Giles asked Master Hopkins. "Who will be our governor now?"

"I do not know," said Master Hopkins, "but the men are having a meeting tomorrow to choose someone. I think that the new governor will be Master William Bradford. He is young, but he has a good head on his shoulders. I should like him for governor."

Just as Master Hopkins had hoped, the men chose William Bradford to be the new governor of Plymouth. Bradford said he would do his best, but he must have someone to help him. Master Isaac Allerton, the tailor, was made his assistant.

Bradford was young and strong. But even for a strong man, the task ahead was a heavy one. The English grains did not grow well in the New World. There were times when the settlers were afraid they would starve. Sometimes they had nothing to eat but shellfish and wild berries and nothing to drink but water.

It was Squanto, the Indian who had stayed with them, who saved the Pilgrims' lives. He taught them how to plant corn.

The children gathered around him as he worked. They had been taught that it was a sin to be idle, and they did their share of the farm labor.

The seed was the same corn that the explorers had taken from the Indians' mounds. But Squanto held no grudge.

The Indian did not sow the corn in rows, as the Pilgrims sowed their wheat. He made little hills, about a foot apart. Then he said, "I shall now show you how to make the ground give life."

The soil, he told the Pilgrims, must have food in it. Plants took food from the soil. Unless more food was put into the soil, a good crop of corn could not be grown in the same ground another year.

But where would the Pilgrims get food? The children looked on breathlessly as Squanto showed them.

The Indian taught the Pilgrims to catch herring in the near-by stream. They would need many herring, he said.

"But what have herring to do with corn?" Henery asked.

Henery and Giles watched Squanto plant the first hill of corn. He put three dead herring on the soft earth, like three spokes in a wheel. Then he placed three kernels of corn near the heads of the fish and covered both fish and corn with earth.

"Now the corn will have food," Squanto told the children.

"But why three fish?" Henery asked.

"Why with their heads toward the center?" Giles wanted to know.

Squanto had an answer. The Indians had always planted corn in this way. It was Indian law. A long time ago, wise people had made the rule. They knew.

"Now the work is done," Henery said as he helped push the soft earth over the last little hill.

"We will have to keep the weeds out," Giles said.

"And the wolves," said Squanto.

Wolves caught the smell of the decaying fish. The wind carried the scent to them. The Pilgrims had to keep watch day and night, or the wolves would have dug up the newly planted corn to get the fish.

Now that the crop was planted, the Pilgrims began to think about the coast to the north of them. They would have to go there if they intended to buy beaver skins from the Indians.

Giles heard some of the men talking about a trading trip. He begged his father to let him and Henery go along.

"We will work hard, Father," Giles promised. "We will take care of the food and the water, and we can load the guns. Please take us along."

"I don't know about Henery," said Master Hopkins. "He is still rather young."

"Oh, do let him come," Giles begged. "He is growing fast. He can work as hard as a man."

The two boys were permitted to go on the trip. They made themselves very useful, building fires and fetching water whenever the shallop landed.

The big sailboat made its way into a broad bay. This bay later became known as Boston Harbor. There were no white people living here now, however. The Pilgrims landed and made friends with the Massachusetts Indians.

"This is a fine place," Master Hopkins told Giles. "There would have been plenty of room for us here. I wish we had landed here instead of at Plymouth. See how rich the soil is."

Giles and Henery had much to tell the other children when they returned to Plymouth.

"We bought some beaver coats from the

the women of the Massachusetts tribe,"
Giles said. "Squanto wanted us to take the
coats by force, but we would not. Besides,
the women were quite willing to sell them."

"That big harbor was a fine place," said
Henery. "I wish that we had gone there
to build our homes."

"No," said Mary Chilton. "God has
chosen Plymouth for us, and here we
shall live and prosper."

The First Thanksgiving

The first summer in the New World had ended. Indian summer was here. The trees were red and gold among the dark pines. The wild grapes were ripe. It was time to bring in the harvest. The English crops of wheat, peas, and barley had not done so well. But the corn crop was very good.

"Have you heard?" Giles asked Henery one morning. "There is to be a Thanksgiving feast. Governor Bradford has said that it will last for three whole days!"

"Won't it be fun?" said Henery. "For once, we shall eat as much as we want!"

The older people also seemed to think that having a feast would be great fun. Giles thought that his mother's step was lighter as she went about her work. She sang happily over the cradle as she rocked Oceanus to sleep.

How much there was to be thankful for! The first dreadful year was over. The Pilgrims knew now that they would not starve in the new land. They were all in good health. There had been no sickness for several months. The clear air, pure water, and work in the fields had done wonders for grownups as well as children.

There were eleven houses now, standing in a straight line along a single street. But it did not matter where one lived. Every person received the same amount of food as the others. The Pilgrims had promised to share everything, and they lived up to their promise.

Best of all, the Pilgrims said to one

another, the people of Plymouth were at peace with their neighbors, the Indians.

"That is what I am most thankful for," Mary Chilton said. She and Henery and Giles were looking for nuts in the woods. They found many kinds — hickory nuts, black walnuts, hazelnuts, and butternuts. It was wonderful to walk among the tall trees and to feel safe from lurking enemies. The dead leaves crunched and rustled under their feet.

"I don't know what we should have done without Squanto and all the other Indians," Giles said to Mary and Henery.

"Yes," said Mary. "Squanto has saved our lives."

"Governor Bradford has to scold him sometimes," Giles said. "Do you know what my father told me? Squanto told the other Indians that we keep the plague hidden under our meetinghouse."

"We don't, do we?" asked Henery.

Giles and Mary laughed. "Of course we don't," Giles said. "But we do have our guns, and the Indians are afraid."

"Surely they know we do not want to harm them," Mary said. "We are all good friends now. In fact, the Indians are coming to our Thanksgiving feast."

"That will be fun," said Henery. "I wonder how they will like prayer meeting," he added thoughtfully. "We are going to give thanks for three days. I am sure we shall spend a lot of time in prayer meetings."

"Never mind, Henery." Mary was laughing at him again. "We shall have time for plenty of feasting, too."

As the day of Thanksgiving drew nearer, the children became more and more excited. There was a pleasant noise of work and talk all up and down the street. Everyone worked, but working for Thanksgiving was fun. There never was an idle moment, never an idle hand.

Giles went hunting with his father and
three of the other men. The hunters
brought back enough ducks and geese to
last a week. Giles and Henery went out to
catch some of the long-legged turkeys that
roamed the woods. How the turkeys
swooshed through the brush! Big as they
were, they could fly up into tall trees.
They made queer shapes against the sky.

The Pilgrims had never eaten turkey before they came to New England. They

still liked roast duck or goose much better.

The smaller boys and girls went out to dig up the bulbs of the wild onions which grew in the low valleys. They also picked water cress in the brooks. Giles's little sister, Damaris, brought back some pretty red berries which she found growing in the bog. They were cranberries. Giles tasted one and made a face.

"Throw them away, Damaris," he told her. "They're much too sour."

The women roasted the geese, ducks, and turkeys on spits in front of the open fires. The little girls kept watch, turning the spits so that the birds should bake to a nice golden brown on all sides.

Stews of clams and other shellfish simmered in pots in front of the great fireplaces. Venison, or deer meat, cooked with vegetables in big tripod kettles. These kettles had legs which stood in the coals.

Every housewife baked bread, both wheat

bread and corn bread. The Pilgrim women had no ovens. They baked their bread in big kettles with tight-fitting lids. The kettles were placed in the coals of the fireplace, and more coals were piled over them.

When it came to mixing the Indian corn pudding, the little girls were allowed to help. Squanto had taught the Pilgrim housewives how to use corn—how to roast fresh ears in the coals, and how to pound the kernels to make corn meal.

Squanto had also taught the Pilgrims to plant squashes and pumpkins in their cornfields. The English people did not like these vegetables when they first ate them. Later, they learned to sweeten them with a little sirup when they cooked them.

The day of Thanksgiving came at last. The Pilgrims were up at dawn, finishing their preparations for the feast. The day was mild and the sun shone brightly. The women covered the tables with their best tablecloths and placed wooden and pewter dishes on them.

The children were helping to set the tables when they heard a sound of drums and trumpets. Massasoit and his braves were coming into town. Captain Standish and some of his men had gone to meet them.

Massasoit had ninety men with him. All the Indians had painted their faces brightly in honor of the feast. They wore trousers and loose shirts made of deerskin.

The Pilgrims sat down on benches and stools near the long tables, while most of their guests squatted on the ground. But

before the feasting could begin, the Pilgrims had to give thanks. Elder Brewster led the people in a long prayer, and then it was Governor Bradford's turn. It seemed to Humility and Henery that the time for eating would never come.

At last the women began to bring out the food. The Pilgrims and their guests filled their plates again and again. They ate heartily of roast fowl, venison stew, clam stew, vegetables, bread, and corn pudding. For dessert there were wild plums and dried berries and a sweet cake.

After awhile the Pilgrims could eat no more. But the Indians were still eating. They had gone without food for days to get ready for the feast.

For three days the Pilgrims and the Indians celebrated this first Thanksgiving festival. When supplies got low, several of the Indians went out and shot a few deer. Then the feasting began again.

Not all the time was spent in eating. Just as Henery had feared, there were long prayer meetings. The Pilgrims gave thanks again and again, and their hearts were truly thankful. All the Indians sat and listened politely, although most of them could not understand one word.

Captain Standish had trained his little army to perform for the occasion. The men marched up and down the street to the beating of the drum.

The Indians showed what they could do, too. They danced the special dances of their tribe, and showed the white men how fast they could run and how high they could jump.

Never had the children had such a good time. Thanksgiving made up for the long months of hard work and hunger.

"We shall celebrate like this every year at harvest time," Giles told Henery. "My father says so."

When the Indians had left at last, the Pilgrims were very tired. But they settled down to work harder than ever. Winter was near, and they must be ready.

The days were growing cold again, and the nights were even colder. The men and boys worked to make the houses snug against the wind and snow.

One chilly day they saw an Indian come into the settlement. He was young and had a fine, strong body. The men saw at once that he was a runner, and that he had a message for them.

"Big Chief," said the Indian. These were the only English words he could say. The men took him to Governor Bradford. Then they went to find Squanto.

"A tall white sail off Cape Cod," Governor Bradford said, thoughtfully, after Squanto had given him the man's message. "Let us hope it is not a French ship, come to raid our settlement."

Captain Standish got his little army ready for action. Every boy who could carry a gun was to help defend the town.

The armed men and boys went up to the top of Fort Hill. They could see the ship now. They fired their cannon as a warning, but still the ship came on. It sailed right into Plymouth Harbor.

Now the Pilgrims could see the ship clearly. They shouted with relief. The British flag floated from its mast. The ship was the *Fortune,* from London.

At last the passengers came ashore. There were thirty-five people on board. The Pilgrims were very happy to see some of their old friends among them.

The newcomers had brought practically no supplies with them. They were expected to make their own way in the New World. The London merchants were still angry that the Pilgrims had sent no cargo when the *Mayflower* returned.

This would be hard on the Pilgrims. After the Thanksgiving feast, they had just enough food to last until the next harvest. Now there were more mouths to feed. Everyone would have to eat less. But the Pilgrims did not complain, except that the children grumbled a little.

"The portion is cut in half again," Humility said as she and Mary Chilton watched the boys chop wood. "Why did we have to eat so much on Thanksgiving? We had more than enough, and now most of it is gone."

"It was well done," Giles answered. "The memory of Thanksgiving will keep us joyful in our hearts all winter."

Indian Neighbors

The *Fortune* left Plymouth about a month later. The ship was well loaded. It carried lumber and fine furs.

It was just as well that the people of Plymouth did not know until later what happened to the *Fortune*. A French pirate ship captured it and took its whole cargo. This was a sad loss, for the furs and lumber on board would have paid half the Pilgrims' debt.

Now the winter winds were blowing cold. The whole colony settled down to its second winter of working and saving.

One day Giles and Henery were gathering kindling in the woods at the edge of town. Through the trees came a strange Indian, striding toward Plymouth. His face was fiercely painted, and he did not smile. His eyes seemed to glitter with hate. Giles and Henery let him pass them, and then followed him back into town.

When the Indian reached the clearing, he stopped and looked about him. Henery and Giles went up to him.

"What are you looking for?" Giles asked bravely.

The Indian stared at him. His expression did not change.

"Squanto," he said at last.

Squanto was not in Plymouth that day. He had gone into the woods to hunt for game. Giles and Henery took the Indian to Governor Bradford's house. The governor looked surprised when he opened the door.

"Big chief," Giles told the Indian.

"What is this?" Governor Bradford asked. "Who is this Indian?"

"He asked for Squanto," Giles said. "He doesn't seem to like us."

The Indian could not speak much English, but he managed to make the governor understand him. He said he had a message from Canonicus, a Narraganset chief. The Narraganset Indians were not very friendly with the tribe of Massasoit.

The message was not a letter. It was a sheaf of arrows, tied with a large snakeskin.

"What does it mean?" Henery whispered to Giles. Both boys could tell from the governor's face that he did not like the message.

Governor Bradford did not know exactly what the message did mean, but he suspected that it meant trouble. Just the same, he welcomed the Indian in a friendly manner. He did not want any more trouble than he could help.

"Go get Captain Standish and Master Winslow," the governor told Henery.

Then he turned to Giles. "Get your father," he said. "And ask your mother to bring the Indian something to eat."

Captain Standish, Master Hopkins, and Master Winslow talked to the Indian for a long time. Mistress Hopkins and the other women brought him food and drink. Finally, after a long visit, the Indian told them all was well.

"Me friend," he said, pointing to his own bare chest. "Narraganset friend."

That afternoon Squanto came back. The Pilgrims showed him the snakeskin.

"Bad," Squanto told them. "Very bad. Narraganset want to make war." The snakeskin, he said, was a challenge.

The Pilgrims knew that they must not let the Narraganset see that they were afraid. The Indians were many, and the white men were few. The Indians feared the white men's guns. But they would not fear them nearly so much if they thought the white men were afraid.

Captain Standish stood before the messenger. "Here!" the little captain said fiercely. "Here is our answer." He gave the Indian the snakeskin. It was filled with powder and bullets now, instead of being tied around a sheaf of arrows.

The Indian seemed afraid to touch the snakeskin. But finally he took it and left Plymouth.

The Pilgrims learned later that the Indian had given the snakeskin to someone else as soon as possible. It passed from one Indian to another. No Indian wanted to keep this white man's magic.

The Narraganset chief sent no more

messages. The Pilgrims had met the challenge bravely. By their courage they had kept trouble away—at least for the present.

Just the same, the word Narraganset made shivers go up and down the children's spines. When Henery and Humility went into the woods now, they glanced back over their shoulders to be sure that no enemy was lurking behind a tree.

One morning in December, the frost hung in the trees like blossoms. Humility and Remember Allerton begged Henery to go into the woods with them to gather pine cones. Pine cones kindled quick fires.

"I'll go if you wait till I finish splitting wood," Henery said.

When he had finished his chore, he picked up one of the pretty baskets the girls had brought. One basket was made of crab shells, and another of reed. These were Indian baskets which the Pilgrims had found when they first landed.

Humility kept running ahead on the trail, shouting, "Here's a bigger one! And here's a bigger one still!"

Henery, lagging behind, heard a sharp bark. A tall, slim Indian boy came striding through the woods. He wore deerskin clothes and carried a tomahawk. He looked very fierce as he swung the light ax in his right hand. Henery thought that he must be a Narraganset.

"Run, Humility! Run, Remember!" cried Henery. "Run home quickly."

The little girls ran, but not toward Plymouth. They ran to Henery. Pine cones tumbled out of their baskets, and Remember's fair hair caught on a twig. Humility, her pigtails bobbing, ran back and broke the branch, for there was no time to untangle the hair.

"What is it?" the girls panted.

Then they saw the Indian and his dog. The dog was a sad brown creature. He slunk against the boy's legs when he saw the children.

"Good dog," Humility said. She was always sorry for anything or anyone that looked sad.

"Dog no good," the Indian declared, shoving the animal with his foot.

The children saw that the dog limped as it moved away from the boy. It had a sore on its leg. There was a frayed rope about its neck.

"Kill dog," the Indian said. He raised his tomahawk.

"No!" cried the girls.

"No!" shouted Henery.

Somehow all three children knew that the Indian did not want to kill his pet.

The ship's doctor on board the *Mayflower* would not have bothered with a dog. But Deacon Fuller knew a little about healing the sick. He was never too weary to care for anything that suffered.

"Let us take him home," Henery begged. "You may come and get him again when he is healed."

The Indian boy looked down at the dog for a long time. Then he said, "Take dog."

He spoke to the dog and then pointed to Henery. Humility reached into her pocket and brought out a piece of corn bread. The dog gulped it down in one swallow.

The children led the dog back home to Plymouth. Whenever they glanced back, they saw the Indian boy still watching.

Deacon Fuller chuckled when the three

children brought him the sad brown dog. But he agreed to do what he could.

The dog stayed with the Pilgrims until he was well. Then, one day while Henery was at school, he ran away into the woods.

"His master must have come for him," Henery told Humility.

Some time later, another Indian came into camp. He was a messenger from Massasoit. He came straight to the governor's house.

"Massasoit is dying," said the Indian.

The news flew from one house to the other. The street was quickly filled with people. Mothers and children rushed out of doorways. Men came hurrying from their work.

"Massasoit is dying?" the men said. "It cannot be. Massasoit is young and strong."

"Corbitant will take his place," Captain Standish told Governor Bradford. "And Corbitant is no friend of ours."

The Pilgrims decided to send Edward

Winslow to see if the news were true. The Indian messenger would go back with him.

Henery and Giles begged Winslow to take them along. Ever since the day when Winslow had gone to meet Massasoit, the boys had admired him. They wanted to be like him when they grew up.

But Winslow refused to take them. The trip was a hard one. And he did not know what kind of a greeting he would get. Massasoit might be dead by the time Winslow reached him.

The Pilgrim and the Indian followed a trail through the forest. In some places the trail was grown over with bushes. Often a wild animal scurried away as the men passed. They waded through brooks. When they came to a deeper stream, the Indian threw a log across it.

Both Winslow and the guide were weary when they reached Corbitant's village. Here they learned that the chief had gone to his village, Sowams. Winslow asked that a runner be sent to see how Massasoit was.

The runner returned at sunset. Massasoit was sinking fast, he said. If Winslow wanted to see him, he must hurry.

The weary men made the most of the sunset. Its red light shone through the trees only a short time. Then the woods became dark. The travelers stumbled on.

As they came closer to Sowams, they began to hear a strange moaning sound.

"That is our people," said the Indian. "They mourn Big Chief."

When the men reached the chief's lodge, Winslow had to push and shove his way through the crowd. The Indians were gathered around Massasoit's bed. They were mourning him with loud shrieks and moans. The medicine men were dancing and adding to the noise with their chant. The squaws wailed as they rubbed the chief's arms and legs.

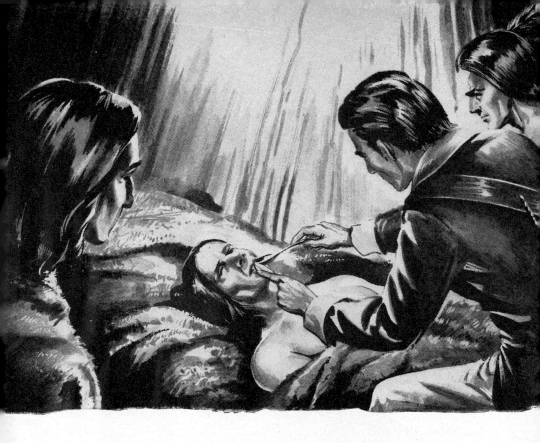

Winslow saw that Massasoit seemed to
be very ill. His teeth were clamped tightly
together, and beads of sweat stood out on
his forehead. But the chief recognized his
white friend and seemed to trust him.

The Pilgrim decided that he might be
able to cure the chief soon. He had brought
a simple medicine which he thought might

help. He forced it between Massasoit's teeth on the point of a knife.

Winslow was doing a dangerous thing, and he knew it. What if he did not help? What if the chief should die? The Indians would blame him.

"The Lord will help me," the Pilgrim thought. "I must do what I can."

To everyone's surprise, even Winslow's, Massasoit was much better in half an hour.

"Good medicine," the Indian chief said. "Give to braves." He insisted that Winslow must give some of the medicine to the men who stood about. Then Massasoit asked for something to eat.

A good sign! The chief was hungry. He wanted soup, good soup like the kind he had eaten in Plymouth. Winslow stewed some sassafras with strawberry leaves and corn. It tasted so good that Massasoit asked for more. This time, he said, Winslow must put a duck in the soup.

Winslow did as the chief asked. He went out and shot a mallard duck, then made it into soup. When the soup was ready, he warned the chief not to eat the grease which floated on top of the broth.

"Be careful," Winslow begged. "You aren't strong enough yet for greasy food."

"I'll eat it just as it is," Massasoit said greedily, and he gulped the soup down. But it was much too rich for him to digest. He became ill again.

Winslow asked all the Indians to be quiet. In a little while, Massasoit felt better. He slept for several hours.

The Indian chief was up and about again in a few days. He seemed as well as ever.

"Never shall I forget what you have done for me," he told Winslow. "You are my friend. You are my own true brother."

When it was time to leave, Corbitant invited Winslow to stop off on his way home and visit him at Buzzard's Bay. This visit would break the journey to Plymouth. Winslow agreed to visit Corbitant.

To the Pilgrim's surprise, Corbitant was gay and pleasant on the journey. He liked to joke and tease. Would Master Winslow come to help him if he were sick, he asked?

"Of course I would," Winslow said. "We love all our neighbors and want to help them any time we can."

"How does it happen, then," asked Corbitant, "that when we visit you, you shoot at us with your guns?"

"That is a salute," Winslow answered. "It is a great honor to be saluted by our guns. That is the way we Pilgrims have of saying 'Welcome' to you."

"I like not such a welcome," Corbitant said soberly.

Home, School, and Church

The Pilgrims felt uneasy after the visit of the Narraganset Indian. They decided to build a high fence, called a stockade, around their town. When the stockade was finished, the Pilgrims felt safer.

The people of Plymouth had plenty to eat now, and their homes were more comfortable. They began to feel as if they had lived in America for a long, long time.

The children of Plymouth had little time for play and chatter. They were expected to work hard. On week days, they went to school or worked at home. Before and after school there were chores to do—feeding the animals, gathering firewood, and helping their parents with farm work and household tasks. Sundays were spent in church.

Henery often stayed at Giles's house overnight. The two boys slept on a straw bed in the loft. The wind whistled through the wall, but there were plenty of covers.

One December morning, Giles nudged Henery awake. "Snow," Giles said. "It has sifted through the chinks in the wall."

"Seems like the middle of the night," Henery complained as he turned over.

"Remember, we have to cut wood for school today," Giles reminded him. "We'll haul it over on the sled, if there's enough snow. You know, if our family doesn't get our share of wood, I will be the one who has to sit farthest from the fire."

Giles shivered as he got out from under the covers and pulled his boots on. He had slept in his clothes, just as Henery had.

Giles reached down, grabbed a handful of snow, and rubbed it into Henery's warm neck. Henery shot out of bed. The two boys scuffled until they heard an angry shout from below.

"Giles!" cried Master Hopkins' deep voice. "That's enough! Come down here and attend to your chores!"

Giles climbed down the rough ladder which led to the main room of the cabin. Henery followed him. Soon Giles had the fire on the hearth stirred up to a good blaze. He swung the kettle over the fireplace and went outside to get wood.

As Giles stepped into the lean-to, the cat purred against his legs, and the goat nudged him. The animals were hungry. Giles fed them and gave them water. Then the two boys chopped wood until Mistress Hopkins called them to breakfast.

Giles's mother was standing in front of the fireplace. She had heated the porridge and the milk. She was turning slices of salt pork in the frying pan, which had a handle almost as tall as Henery.

Master Hopkins took his place at one end of the table. His wife sat down beside him. She held the baby in her lap.

As the children came in, Mistress Hopkins said "Good morning" to each of them. The younger children sat down on benches along both sides of the table. The table was long and narrow, and the Pilgrims called it a "board." Henery sat with Giles at the end opposite Master and Mistress Hopkins.

The children knew better than to fidget during the long morning prayers. Even when breakfast began, there was little talking. The children drank milk and ate porridge. The grownups ate the meat.

Henery ate his porridge with a pewter spoon. His dish was a trencher—a square block of wood which was hollowed out in the center. He looked at the pewter plates and candlesticks which stood in a row above the fireplace. Some day, Henery thought, he would have pewter dishes like those the Hopkins family had brought from England.

"The wolves will soon be howling about the settlement," Master Hopkins said in his deep voice. "You know, Giles, this year I think I shall give you one of the guns for your own."

Both Giles and Henery were growing fast. Soon Giles would be an officer in Captain Standish's little army.

"I have never shot a wolf," Henery said to Giles in a low voice. "I wish I had a gun."

Master Hopkins heard him. "This year you shall shoot a wolf, Henery," he said. "You

TRENCHER

PORRINGER

KETTLE

SKILLET

are growing old enough now to learn how to use a gun. I shall take you with us when Giles and I go hunting."

Henery was so excited he could hardly sit still. "Oh, thank you, Master Hopkins!" he said. He would really go hunting with the big boys and the men! Perhaps he would shoot a wolf himself! He could hardly wait to tell Bartholomew Allerton, who sat next to him in school.

There was no public school in Plymouth. But Giles and Henery and some of the other boys went to a private school. Some of the Pilgrims paid the schoolmaster to teach their sons reading, writing, and arithmetic.

The smaller children were taught to read by their parents. They studied their letters from hornbooks. A hornbook was a flat piece of wood with a handle at one end. A piece of paper with letters and words printed on it was fastened to the wood. Over the paper went a thin sheet of horn, made from the horn of an animal. The children could read the letters and words through the cover. A sheet of paper lasted a long time when used in this way—and paper was scarce.

Oceanus, Giles's little brother, was still studying his letters from the hornbook. But Giles's sisters did not have lessons any more. Mistress Hopkins taught them to sew, weave, and spin. The Pilgrims did not believe that girls needed much education.

"I am glad that I do not have to go to school," Damaris said, as the boys wrapped up warmly to go out.

"I don't mind school so much," Henery said. "I like to read. Some day I shall read all the books in Elder Brewster's library."

"That is a lot of books, to be sure," Master Hopkins said, laughing. "And some of them are in Greek and Latin. Elder Brewster is quite a scholar."

It was still dark and foggy when Giles and Henery started to school. The steep, thatched roofs made the houses look as if they were huddling close to the ground. Whenever a door opened, Henery saw the flickering light from log fires. He could not look into the houses through the windows, for they were made of oiled paper.

Giles pulled a sled behind him, loaded with a good supply of firewood. He had made the sled himself by placing two wooden runners under a wooden box. The runners slid along easily over the new snow.

When Giles and Henery arrived at school, they took their places in the classroom, which was also the main room of the schoolmaster's house. The boys sat on benches behind long tables. Henery sat between Giles and Bartholomew Allerton.

The teacher was a tall, dignified man with a dark, well-kept beard. His clothes were black. The boys were afraid of him, for he was quick to punish, but they respected him for his knowledge. He had once studied at one of the English universities.

School began with a long, solemn prayer. Then the boys sang a hymn. Next came the arithmetic lesson. The boys recited their numbers together, in chorus.

The next lesson was the reading lesson— Henery's favorite part of the long school day. Today, as usual, the boys took turns reading aloud. One boy after another stood in front of the class and read a few verses from the Bible.

Henery could not keep his mind on the reading today. He kept thinking of what Master Hopkins had said at breakfast. What fun it would be to shoot a wolf! Henery could not help leaning over to tell Bartholomew about it.

"Master Bartholomew is whispering," said the master in a voice like thunder. "Come forward, Master Bartholomew. You

HORNBOOK

BIRCH SWITCH

DUNCE CAP

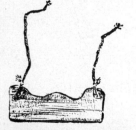

WHISPERING STICK

shall wear the whispering stick until noon."

Bartholomew got up without a word.

"No, master," Henery said quickly. "It was not Bartholomew's fault. I spoke to him. I was telling him about the wolf I am going to shoot this winter."

The boys looked as if they would like to laugh. But they did not dare, or the master would punish them all.

"Very well, Master Henery," said the schoolmaster. "You shall wear the whispering stick. And you and Master Bartholomew shall both have a whipping after school."

Henery wanted to protest at so much punishment, but he knew it would be no use. He hated the whispering stick. He would much rather the master had whipped him at once, with the birch switch that he always kept handy. A whipping lasted only a few minutes, though it hurt when the birch twigs came down on his back.

The whispering stick was made from a block of wood. It had two cords attached to it, one at each end. The block of wood went into Henery's mouth, and the cords were tied tightly around his head. Henery wondered if a horse felt this way when it had a bit in its mouth.

After school, the master whipped both Henery and Bartholomew. Then he told Bartholomew to go home.

"Let this be a lesson to you," the master said sternly. "As for Master Henery, I would speak with him further."

Henery did not know what to think. Surely he had been punished enough!

When he was alone with the boy, the

master seemed to become kinder. But his voice was still stern.

"Master Henery," he said, "you do not seem to be able to keep your mind on your work. Perhaps our studies are too easy for you."

Henery did not know what to say. It was true that the work seemed easy to him, but how could he say so?

"Monday," said the master, "you shall begin to study Latin." Then, seeing how happy Henery looked, he added, "I shall expect you to work hard and to pay strict attention, mind you. Else the lessons shall stop at once."

"Oh, thank you, thank you!" Henery cried. He was very happy. Soon he would be able to read the Latin books in Elder Brewster's library.

The next day was Sunday. Henery and Giles went to church with their neighbors early in the morning. Everyone wore his best clothes. The men put their heavy boots away and wore low shoes with plain buckles. The girls and their mothers wore their best bonnets, which tied under their chins.

The Pilgrims had not yet built a church. The one-story house which stood at the top of Fort Hill served as their church. This building was also the fort, town hall, and jail. It did not look like a church. It was low and square, and was built of heavy oak beams.

The cannons were mounted on the roof of the fort. Muzzles of guns poked out of openings in the thick walls.

This Sunday, as usual, the beating of drums called the people to worship. There were no bells, but the people could hear the drums in all the houses of Plymouth. Each man came out of his house with his musket in his hand.

No one was late. Men, women, and children met at Captain Standish's house at the foot of the hill. Then, three by three, the Pilgrims marched up the steep slope to the meetinghouse. Governor Bradford came last, walking with the preacher and Captain Standish.

Once inside the fort, the men set their guns down, but they kept them within reach. The men sat on the right, the women on the left. The very small children sat on stools at their mothers' feet.

Henery found it hard to stay awake during the long sermon. The wooden bench was hard, and there was nothing to lean against. Henery watched the tithingman walk down the aisle. It was the tithingman's duty to see that people behaved properly in church. He carried a long pole, with a squirrel's tail at one end and a hard, round knob at the other.

A woman was nodding. Henery saw her wake with a start as the tithingman tickled the end of her nose with the squirrel's tail.

Henery could not help laughing aloud. The next moment he felt the knob come down hard on his head—so hard that tears came to his eyes.

Henery looked straight ahead now, trying to listen to every word of the sermon. He knew that later he would have to answer questions about it.

The morning meeting was over at last. The women began to prepare the noon meal. While the children ate, a deacon

questioned them about the sermon. Another long service took up the whole afternoon. Then everyone went home to supper.

Henery had heard the men talking together very seriously during the noon meal. Some of them said that Massasoit was no longer a friend. But Henery knew this could not be. The Indian chief would be a friend to the Pilgrims as long as he lived.

The week was over. Tomorrow there would be school and work again. But now Henery had something to look forward to—in fact, two things. He would study Latin—and he would have a chance to shoot a wolf.

Adventure in Boston

From the time that Plymouth boys could handle a hoe, they worked in the cornfields. The Pilgrims had to have plenty of corn for trading with the Indians. The Indians always needed corn, and they were willing to trade beaver skins for it. The Pilgrims wanted as much beaver as they could get. They were still paying on the debt they owed to the London merchants.

"The more corn we plant," Giles said, "the more beaver skins we can buy."

Giles and Henery worked together in the fields all through the summers. There was flax to grow as well as corn. While they were still children, the boys helped to plant the seeds. Then they watched the blue flowers blossoming.

Soon the flowers became seed pods. The boys sprinkled the seeds into pieces of cloth, to save them for the next planting. They liked to see the seeds fill the wooden pails when they shook out the cloths.

The easiest part of the work was to pull out the flax plants and tie them in bundles. The next step was carrying the bundles to the brook. The boys sprinkled the bundles with water every single day. The green stalks had to rot. After the rotten part had come off, the plant fiber was made into linen thread.

The boys hated the smell of the rotting flax. But the hardest part of the work was still to be done. The soft part of the flax fiber had to be separated from the hard, woody part.

First, the men placed the plant fiber between the jaws of the flax brake. The brake was a wooden frame with two sets of wooden slats that fitted together when the frame was closed. Then the men beat the flax with a heavy knife called a swingle. Next came the hackling. The hackles were square slabs of wood with wire teeth set closely together. The flax was drawn through these teeth.

At last the flax was ready for spinning. When it lay on the floor in coarse brown bundles, the girls knew it was time for their part of the work. Humility and all the other girls learned to use the spinning wheel as soon as they were big enough to make it turn.

As she spun the thread, Humility sat in front of the wheel. She pumped the pedal that turned the wheel with her foot and guided the thread with one hand. The turning of the wheel made the thread wind

FLAX BRAKE

FLAX SWINGLE

SPINNING WHEEL

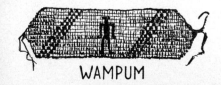

WAMPUM

around a bobbin. Humility had to keep wetting the flax as she worked.

After the spinning, the thread was bleached, and after the bleaching came the weaving. The women and the older girls wove the cloth on great wooden looms. Then they dyed it. The Pilgrims did their work together and farmed their land together. Every man, woman, and child knew that it paid to work hard. When the corn was harvested, they could buy beaver skins with it. The skins could be sent to London. Then ships would come back to Plymouth, bringing supplies.

A great change came in 1627. The Indians no longer wanted to buy so much corn. They wanted strings of beads called wampum. The beads were made of shells. Wampum was white, purple, or black in color. The Indians liked the black best. They used the wampum for ornaments and for trading with other tribes.

"It's hard to think of these strings of shell beads as money," the Pilgrims said.

Wampum *was* money, though—Indian money. If an Indian had a lot of wampum, he was rich.

The Pilgrims bought their first wampum from a Dutch trader. Afterward they were sorry, for they could not understand why the Indians would want these worthless beads. But they were delighted when they saw how much beaver they could buy with the wampum.

The Pilgrims themselves were not rich. Their colony did not grow fast. They stayed at home and carried on trade with the Indians and with ships that came into their harbor.

But the Pilgrims had neighbors now. New colonies were growing up north and south of them. These colonies began to buy from Plymouth. They bought corn, goats, cattle, and hay. The Pilgrims thought it would be a good idea to raise more of everything, so that they could sell more to their neighbors.

Ten miles away from Plymouth, on the north shore of Plymouth Bay, there was some very good land. Henery and Giles went hunting there one day. The place was called Ducksburrow, because wild ducks had their nests there. Henery and Giles found the trails rough and muddy, and ten miles was a long way to walk. But they noticed that the land looked richer than that at Plymouth.

"Why shouldn't some of us move?"

Henery said to Giles. "Captain Standish and John Alden want to take up farms at Ducksburrow. They want to build a new town there. The Brewster boys, Love and Wrestling, want to go, too."

"Governor Bradford is against it," Giles said. "He fears that the colony will be weakened if any of the people move away."

"But those at Ducksburrow will still be a part of the colony," Henery said. "If Plymouth Plantation is to grow, there must be more than one town."

"My father agrees with you," Giles said.

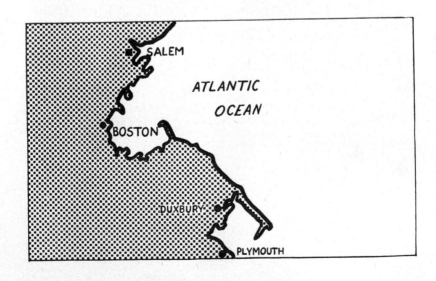

Henery and Giles were young men now. Henery was engaged to marry a pretty young girl named Ann Plummer. He and Ann decided they would live on a farm at Ducksburrow. This town later became known as the village of Duxbury.

The land was divided. The Pilgrims laid out a street in the new town. They built houses and plowed fields. There was plenty of work ahead, but the Pilgrims did not mind work.

Master Brewster moved out to Ducksburrow to live there with his sons, Love and Wrestling. John and Priscilla Alden lived at Ducksburrow with their children. Captain Miles Standish had a farm at the foot of a hill. People called it "Captain's Hill."

Henery and Ann were married. They settled down together to hard work. Their farm prospered.

On Sundays Henery, Ann, and the other people of Ducksburrow went to Plymouth to attend church. They went in pouring rain, baking heat, or biting snow. Sometimes they went by boat, but when the sea was too rough they had to walk, or ride on the backs of slow oxen.

Often Henery would be so tired when he reached Plymouth that he could not keep his eyes open during the service. After the long day of worship would come the trip home. Then there would be the evening chores to do.

"I don't see why we can't have a church at home," Henery said on his way home from worship one Sunday evening.

"Yes," said John Alden. "There are so many of us here now. Surely we can worship God at Ducksburrow as well as at Plymouth."

"Governor Bradford feels that we ought to worship together," Elder Brewster told the group. "He fears that we will grow apart and change our ways."

Finally, in 1637, the Plymouth Pilgrims
agreed to let the people of Ducksburrow
build a church at home. Life became much
easier. There were children now in Henery's cottage. They helped with the chores
just as Henery had done when he was a
little boy.

Henery's old friend Richard More had
moved to Salem. He had married a girl

named Christian Hunt, and his farm was prospering.

Giles and Henery often spoke of Richard when Henery came to Plymouth.

"I would like to see him," said Henery. "And I would like to see Salem, too. They say it is a fine town."

One day in late fall Henery received a letter from Richard. Richard wanted to buy some farm animals from his friend—a goat and some cattle. Henery decided that this would be a good chance to go to Salem and visit Richard. Giles decided to go with him. The young men would travel on foot, at least as far as Boston. They would stop in Boston to do some business.

The day before the journey, Henery was in Plymouth. He spent the night with Giles at the Hopkins house. The two young men began their trip early the next morning.

The steep roofs of the houses were covered with white frost as Henery and Giles walked down the long main street of the town. The young men felt gay and happy. Their crops were gathered, and they were free to enjoy their journey.

Smoke rose from the chimneys. Henery and Giles caught glimpses of firelight through the doors and windows. Whenever a door opened, the flickering light from log fires showed families gathered around their hearths. In one cottage Henery saw a woman at a spinning wheel.

Far less pleasant was the sight the young men saw at the end of the street. A middle-aged man sat with his feet locked into a wooden frame. This frame was called the stocks. Beside it was the pillory, but no one was being punished there today. The pillory had holes for the neck and wrists.

The man's nose looked blue with cold.

"Poor fellow," Giles said.

"He would best keep the Sabbath after this," said Henery.

"I did but miss one sermon," the man wailed pitifully.

His whimpering followed the young men as they hurried out of the town. Looking back, they saw smoke rising straight into the air from the chimneys.

"It's going to be a pleasant day," said Henery.

The sun was just beginning to spread its

light through the red and yellow oaks and maples and the dark evergreens. The forest looked as if it had been pushed back to make room for the farms. And the farms clustered around the town, as if for protection. The Pilgrims still built their houses close together, because it was safer.

The trip was long and hard. The young men had to follow narrow Indian trails. By the time they reached Boston, Henery and Giles had decided that they would go the rest of the way by boat.

The young men spent almost a whole day exploring Boston. They had heard a great deal about the town. Boston was only seven years old, but already it was growing into a real city.

Boston was built on three hills. It was full of winding lanes, which ran around boulders and skirted damp places. Giles and Henery followed one of these lanes. To their surprise, they found themselves on a grassy meadow with cows all around them.

Giles called to a small boy who was coaxing a cow homeward with his stick. "Where are we, friend?"

"You're on Boston Common," the boy laughed. "Where else would you be?"

"Can you tell us where Samuel Cole lives?" Henery asked.

"King Street," the boy said, pointing.

As they walked on, Henery said suddenly, "This must be where John Harrison, the roper, lives."

Giles looked back to a lane which had been sanded quite recently. Then he saw what Henery was looking at. It was a large house with a big side yard. A boy of about fourteen was backing away from a noisy, turning wheel. This wheel was spinning strands of hemp into rope. The boy held the rope in his hands. He backed farther and farther away from the wheel as the strands grew longer and longer.

"Good day!" Henery called. "Takes a lot of room to spin rope, doesn't it?"

"It does indeed!" the boy shouted back, without stopping his work.

Samuel Cole's shop was in his house. The customers warmed themselves at his fireplace and sat chatting on benches. There

were shelves everywhere, it seemed to the young men from Plymouth. There were broad counters, too, and a case of sweets.

A bearded man with bright blue eyes served the customers. He rolled out barrels of apples, cut down hams from the rafters, plucked chickens, and wrapped up cabbages.

When Henery and Giles stepped up to the counter, Master Cole met them with a broad smile.

"You're strangers here, aren't you?" he asked. "Come far?"

"Yes," said Henery. "From Plymouth, and all the way by foot."

"Quite a trip," said the storekeeper.

Henery asked to see the linens, and Master Cole brought them out.

"Basket pattern, bird's-eye, and oak leaf," he pointed out. "Some like one, some like another."

Henery decided on the bird's-eye pattern. He thought that Ann would like it.

"Plenty of napkins needed in a big family," Mr. Cole said. "They say the governor has a fork. His family wouldn't have to wash so many napkins if they used a fork for eating their food."

"Fork?" The travelers from Plymouth laughed at the idea. The only forks they knew about were pitchforks for hay.

They asked Master Cole to direct them to the inn. They were to leave for Salem the next morning.

At the inn, a great oak door admitted them to an enormous room. At the far end of the room was the largest fireplace they had ever seen. The air was full of pipe smoke and the odor of roasting meat. Men sat at rough tables, talking and smoking and waiting for their dinner. Several newcomers warmed their legs near the fire.

One handsome young man wore a purple velvet coat trimmed with braid. He bent forward to use the tongs which hung on a hook above the hearth. Gracefully he took a coal from the fire and lit his pipe with it. A gold ring shone on his finger. Henery and Giles stared at him. They had never seen such splendor.

A man in a white apron stood near the fire. He was watching a large goose that was roasting on the spit. The man turned the spit as he smeared fat on the goose's brown skin.

Giles and Henery came forward.

"Good sir," Henery asked, "may we have lodgings for the night?"

"I'm the cook, sir," the man said. "Go through that door over there and you'll find the landlord."

The landlord was a big man. He wore a velvet coat with a fine lace collar, and he had a loud, booming voice. He begged the young men from Plymouth to make themselves comfortable and have dinner. A bed would be made ready for them upstairs.

A little later, Henery and Giles sat at the long table with other guests. Meat and bread were served, and milk to drink. Then came corn pudding. The handsome young man ate at a small table by himself.

Giles nudged Henery, and Henery looked sideways. The man was eating very daintily. He was cutting his meat in tiny pieces and placing each piece in his mouth with the point of his knife.

"We'll have a lot to tell the people back home in Plymouth," Henery said.

"Yes," said Giles. "Home is not much like Boston."

"The corn pudding tastes just the same," Henery said, putting a spoonful in his mouth. "In fact, I think Ann's is better."

A Visit in Salem

The boat trip to Salem was pleasant after the long walk from Plymouth to Boston. Henery and Giles made the journey on a ship which had called at Boston. Before night, the ship docked in Salem Harbor.

Henery and Giles stopped at the inn to ask their way to Richard's house.

"Master Richard More has been expecting you," the innkeeper said. "His house is yonder."

Now Richard was coming toward them, waving and shouting. He took them into his house. Henery had heard that Richard was doing well, but he did not know that his old friend had so pleasant a home.

The great room was like his own house in Ducksburrow. It was kitchen and living-room for Richard and his family. The broom, fire tongs, and long-handled skillets looked new. There were fine chests and large armchairs made of smooth wood.

Pitchers and porringers of pewter stood next to a row of pewter plates on the heavy oak lintel above the fireplace. The fireplace was made of rough bricks, set into a white-washed frame. The floor had been scrubbed and sanded.

Christian, Richard's wife, was also glad to see the two friends from Plymouth. The Mores had two children, a baby boy in the cradle and a little girl of about two. Henery and Giles admired them, and Henery told Christian about his own children.

"The boy is Jasper, and the girl is Ellen," Richard told them. "I named them after my little brother and sister, who died. I have never forgotten that first winter in Plymouth."

"Richard can hardly remember London," Christian said. She was working quickly and skillfully as she prepared supper. "But he remembers the trip over, even though he was such a little boy."

"I remember it, too," Henery said. "Remember Squanto, Richard, and how we loved him? And how sad we all felt when he died?"

The More family and the guests sat down at the long table. Just as in Plymouth, the corn pudding came first.

"Squanto showed us how to make corn pudding," Richard said. "He even taught us how to make corn meal. I don't know what we should have done without him."

"Yes," said Giles, "but my father told me that they had a lot of trouble with Squanto. He stirred up quarrels with the

Indians. He made them pay him for protecting them against us. Once he made so much trouble that Massasoit wanted us to send him to Sowams, to be punished."

"I never heard about that," Richard said. "What happened?"

"Oh, Governor Bradford wouldn't do it. Squanto begged to be forgiven. And we couldn't let him be killed. He had done so much to help us."

"Yes," Henery said, "and we will always be grateful."

"Christian, you make the best Indian pudding I've ever tasted," Giles told Richard's young wife.

A little later, Henery said, "You make the best stew, Christian."

The young woman laughed. "You must be very hungry," she said, "but I thank you kindly."

"The Indians no longer love us as they did," Richard said, still thinking of Squanto.

"They say we destroy their hunting with our farms."

"They are not far wrong," said Giles. "We do want more and more land, for more people are coming from England every year. And as more people come, the Indians will hate us more and try to kill us. It is too bad, but we shall have to fight."

"Yes," Henery said. "That is why we

want to send help to the people of Connecticut. They are fighting the Pequot Indians. If they are not safe, we in Plymouth will not be safe either."

"I hear that Master Winslow went to Boston to talk to Governor Winthrop about sending help to Connecticut," Richard said. "I have always loved Master Winslow. And the Indians love him, too. He is a fine man."

"Master Winslow has moved to Green's Harbor," Henery told him. "His home is called Careswell. He named it after the Winslow home in England."

"Plymouth has several towns now, I hear," Richard said. "The colony is still growing."

"But not nearly as fast as Salem," said Giles. "Or Boston."

The meal was finished now. Richard suggested that they go out and look at the town. He and Henery could talk about their business later.

The Pilgrims from Plymouth were very much interested in Salem. The people who had settled there were called Puritans. The Puritans received this name because they wanted to purify the English church. The English government punished these Puritans for their opinions, so thousands of them came to New England. Some of them had settled in Boston.

Salem had many houses which looked strange to the visitors. There were cottages like Richard's, and there were also some strange-looking houses which were called wigwams.

"Wigwams!" Giles cried. "But how different they look from Indian wigwams!"

The settlers had had only simple tools to work with, but how they had worked! They had cut green hickory saplings. Then they had sharpened the young trees at one end. The trees were driven into the ground, side by side, like stakes. The poles were then

bent and tied together at the top. They made a long, arched roof. The frame of the house was covered with woven mats.

"Did you ever see such weaving?" Henery asked Giles. "Not at all like the mats the Indians weave for their wigwams."

"They've put pine bark over the mats," Giles pointed out. "They've laid it like shingles. This wigwam will last a long time. Indians move much too often to build wigwams as nice as this one."

A woman came to the door of the wigwam. "Won't you come in, neighbor?" she
said. "Bring your guests with you."

The young men stepped through the door
after Richard. At the far end of the wigwam they saw the fireplace. It filled the
entire end of the house.

"It's built of stones," Richard said.
"They're stuck together with mortar made
of pounded oyster and clam shells."

Henery was very much interested. The

fireplace looked very strong. Over it, a piece of great rough log served as lintel. The chimney was also made of field stone.

"The Indian wigwams I have seen," said Henery, "just have a cleared place in the middle of the floor. The smoke gets out through openings between the poles. This is ever so much better."

"Indeed it is," said the woman. "Won't you sit down?"

Giles and Henery seated themselves on stools near the long, narrow table.

Henery pointed to the door at the end of the wigwam opposite the fireplace. It was a sturdy door, made of three heavy boards, two of pine and one of oak. The blacksmith had made the nails, Richard told them.

"No Indian wigwam ever had a door like that," said Henery.

"A door is much better than a deerskin or a piece of cloth," the woman said.

She seemed happy and comfortable in her wigwam. As they left, she called out, "Oh, Master More, do show the Plymouth guests our dugouts. They are very warm."

Richard thanked her and led his visitors along the lane. He pointed out that all the houses had their backs to the north wind.

"A good idea," Giles said. "I keep my back to the north wind myself, when it blows cold."

The dugouts were houses that were built into the sides of hills or into banks of earth. The fireplace chimneys rose above the hills and banks.

Richard took his guests to visit a family who lived in one of these houses. The housewife and her children were excited when they saw the visitors from Plymouth. They gave the young men pieces of fresh gingerbread.

"I don't blame Richard for moving to Salem," said Giles. "The food is so good."

The two travelers were tired when they went to bed that evening in Richard's loft. They slept soundly. It was late in the morning when Christian awakened them.

"Richard wants to show you more of Salem," she said when they came down to breakfast.

"Yes," Henery said, "and Richard and I still haven't settled our business. It is time we were up. But our bed was very comfortable, Christian."

Richard had been talking with Giles. Now he said, "Come on, Henery. You must be finished with your breakfast by this time, and it's almost time for my dinner. Let us go out and see the flakes."

The flakes, Henery found, were flat fields where codfish were laid on round stones to dry. The people of Salem sent the dried fish to England, where they were exchanged for cloth and other things. The Pilgrims had never caught enough codfish to make fishing an important trade. But in Salem the fish was so important that the people called it "King Cod."

Henery and Giles found the flakes very interesting. They looked at the fields for a while and then walked on with Richard.

A woman with a pleasant face tended a kettle outside a cottage. From the kettle rose an unpleasant smell of boiling grease and lye.

"Soap!" Henery exclaimed. "I suppose she makes it the way Ann does. Ann pours water into a pail filled with wood ashes. Then the liquid is let out into another pail called a piggin."

"My mother used to pour water through wood ashes until the mixture was strong enough to float an egg," Giles said. "By the time the soap was made, there was always plenty of washing to do. It certainly was handy to have the brook so close. Mother would hang the clothes on the bushes to dry. We always helped her."

The woman at the kettle heard them.

"I wish we had a brook," she said. "We have to carry our water."

The young men looked at the stocks and the pillory as they passed down the main street. Today there was no unhappy person in either place.

"And now the Governor's house!" Richard said proudly. He had saved the governor's house for last. Giles and Henery thought it was very splendid. Thirty-two oak trees had been cut down to provide lumber for the house. The diamond-shaped window panes had come from England.

"We have nothing like that in Plymouth," Giles said.

Giles and Henery stayed in Salem with Richard for several days. Then they took a boat back to Plymouth. Henery promised to send Richard the animals he wanted in the spring.

"Why don't you bring Christian and the children to Ducksburrow to visit us?" Henery asked Richard. "Ann would like very much to see you."

"Yes," said Giles. "And my mother and father would like to see you, too. They asked to be remembered to you."

Richard sighed. "I wish we could come," he said. "And maybe we shall. Maybe some day our children will be friends."

On the morning that Giles and Henery left, Christian packed a good lunch for them to eat on the boat. The friends said good-by to one another rather sadly. They knew it might be a long time before they met again.

"Take care of yourselves," Richard said. "And remember me to your father and mother, Giles. They were always very kind to me."

"We won't forget you, or Salem," Henery told Christian. "And we won't forget your kindness. Some day we shall meet again."

Back Home in Plymouth

Henery came to see Mary Winslow a few days after he and Giles returned from Salem. Mary Chilton had married John Winslow ten years before, and she and John had several children. Henery and Giles and Mary were still very good friends. Henery and Giles liked John, too. He was wise and kind, just like his older brother, Edward Winslow.

Henery stopped in to see the Winslows whenever he was in Plymouth. Usually he came alone, for Ann stayed in Ducksburrow with the children.

Today Henery found Mary busy with candle making. Her children had gathered huge sacks of bayberries. Henery had sniffed the fresh, sweet smell of the little gray berries as he came along the street. In almost every house, women were boiling them with wax to make candles.

Mary was working hard when Henery came in. He sat down to visit and to help. In one corner was a great pile of flax wicks. A little girl was putting the wicks in even rows. Mary began to tie them on short poles, about four inches apart. Then she laid the poles across the backs of two straight chairs.

"Be careful of the hot wax, Sarah," she told the little girl.

Little Sarah moved away from the kettle of hot wax which stood beside her mother's chair. She listened shyly as her mother and Henery talked about his trip to Salem and Boston.

"The best part of the whole trip," Henery told Mary, "was coming home to Ann and the children, and to Plymouth."

Henery watched Mary lift the stick to which the wicks were tied. She dipped the wicks in the hot mixture and raised the stick again very carefully. Then she set it across the chairs once more. Over and over Mary dipped the wicks on each stick. Soon the little wicks began to look like candles.

"Mother doesn't get tired," the child said to Henery.

"No," Mary told her daughter. "I do not. These are company candles. When I make them I think of merriment—of guests and good friends."

"May I put them in the candle-box?" little Sarah asked.

"Let me do something," Henery begged. Mary gave him some nuts to crack. They were hazelnuts her children had gathered in the woods.

Mary worked skillfully and carefully as she made her candles. Some housewives started candles with bayberry wax, then finished them with common tallow. But Mary used a mixture of bayberry wax and beeswax.

The Pilgrims did not always use candles for light, for candles were too precious. Often they picked up pine knots in the woods. These knots burned with a bright, smoky flame, for they were full of pine resin. They were like torches.

The only kind of lamp the Pilgrims had was called a Betty lamp. This lamp was like a shallow saucer, with a chain to hang it by at one side and a wick at the other. The saucer was filled with oil, usually whale oil, and the wick was lighted.

Candles, Betty lamps, and pine knots gave light that was good enough to work by. The Pilgrims did not do much reading or writing after sundown.

Henery told Mary about Richard's house, and about the fine houses of Boston.

"We do quite as well here," Mary boasted. "Have you seen my canopy bed? It came all the way from England."

Henery had not seen the canopy. Little Sarah trailed along as Mary led him into another room. There stood a four-poster bed with curtains drawn close around it.

"Here is my new warming pan," Mary said. The warming pan was very handsome. People placed hot coals in a warming pan just before they went to bed. Then they slid the pan between the cold sheets to take the chill off the bedding.

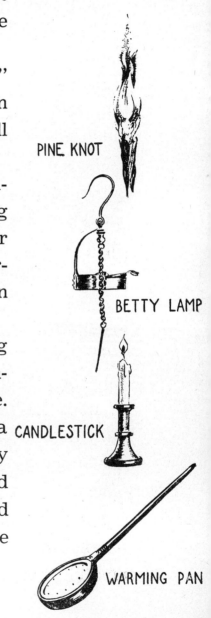

PINE KNOT

BETTY LAMP

CANDLESTICK

WARMING PAN

"You did not notice my new pewter plates," Mary said, as they came back into the kitchen. "And my new candlesticks."

"They have lots of candlesticks in Boston," Henery said, teasingly. "Boston isn't much like Plymouth."

Mary's face grew rosy. "Boston was all boulders and blueberry bushes when we people in Plymouth were snug and comfortable," she said. "But just the same, John and I will live in Boston some day."

"Ann and I will visit you there," Henery promised.

That winter there was much to be thankful for. Spinning wheels were seldom silent in Plymouth. Someone was always busy at a loom. Grandmothers who could no longer do heavy work enjoyed making new patterns.

The men were often away on hunting or fishing or trading trips. Farther south, whaling was becoming an important trade.

Plymouth was now a settled colony, with other colonies growing up all around it. Fishing, hunting, trapping, building! All over New England one could hear the sound of the hammer and the ax. A nation was being built.

The *Mayflower* children, grown up now, were taking part in the building. They were trying to do it without harming the Indians.

There was not one of the Pilgrims who forgot Samoset and his greeting, "Welcome." Henery never forgot how Squanto had shown the children how to pop corn. Now Mary's and Henery's children popped corn and munched apples during the long winter evenings.

The Indians did not like the noise of the mills. They said it frightened the birds and the deer. They did not like to see the trees cut down, for the great forests gave shelter to the animals they hunted.

When the Pilgrims met each other at town meetings or at church they often talked about the Indians. The Pilgrims were at peace with their neighbors, but the people of Connecticut were still fighting the Pequot War. The Pilgrims felt that their colony might be attacked.

Just the same, Thanksgiving was a happy holiday that fall. The Pilgrims believed that there would be many more Thanksgivings, each better than the last. Winter, these days, meant good stores of food, cheeses ripening on the shelves, pleasant fires, and time for visiting.

The winter soon passed. Early in the spring came sugar making. Nearly everyone in Plymouth, old and young, helped to make maple sugar.

Henery brought his children from Ducksburrow for the sugar making. He and Giles cut spouts from soft wood. They made slashes in the tree trunks and placed a

spout in each cut. On the spouts they
hung buckets. The sweet maple sap
dripped into the buckets.

The children worked along with the
grownups. Their merry voices rang through
the woods. They found it fun to run from
tree to tree and empty the buckets into
barrels. Then the barrels were placed on

a sledge. Master Hopkins' mare, the only horse in Plymouth, pulled the sledge through the snow.

There was work for everyone. Some of the boys kept the fires going under the pans of sap. The women watched the cooking very carefully. When the sap began to get thick, most of it was poured off.

"The first sirup is always the best," Mary Winslow declared.

Now the thick sirup was poured into the pans. Some of the pans were oblong, like bricks, and some were round, with fluted edges.

Giles was calling.

"Come on, everybody! Come on, children! Let's make candy in the snow!"

The children poured a little hot, thick sirup on the clean white snow. Soon they had delicious, chewy maple candy.

On days like this it seemed to the Pilgrims that all their hard times were over.

One evening in early spring, Giles was having supper with the Winslows.

Sugar making was over now. Mary served maple sirup on her corn pudding. Her table linen was snowy white, and her bayberry candles burned steadily in the pewter candlesticks. Firelight flickered over the stew of good meat and vegetables and the bowl of red apples.

"I hoped Henery would come in today," Mary said, "but he did not."

"He has gone scouting," her husband told her. "At least, so Governor Bradford told me. He has gone with Captain Standish and some of the others from Ducksburrow."

"Why?" asked Mary.

"To make sure that all is well with the Indians," Giles answered. His father had told him that day that the Pilgrim leaders were worried. They feared that some of the Narraganset Indians might join with the Pequot Indians in the Pequot War.

Even as he spoke there came a heavy pounding on the door. John Winslow went to open it. Young Peregrine White stood at the door. He was very much excited.

"Indians!" he cried. "I saw them from Fort Hill. The woods are full of them!"

John Winslow was on his feet in a moment. He took his gun from its place on the wall.

"Help yourselves," cried John. "I've enough firearms for all. Is there time to reach the fort?"

"I fear not," Peregrine answered. "I stopped at the governor's. He said to stay where we were. He does not believe there will be trouble. But we never know. Darken the house and hide the children. Warn them not to make any noise."

Meanwhile, Henery was walking through the woods, on his way to Plymouth. He was alone, for Captain Standish and the others had gone home to Ducksburrow.

Just as Henery came to the stockade, he heard a soft sound which made him turn. In the dusk he saw someone slip behind a tree. His heart beat loud with fear. He realized that there were Indians all around him.

Suddenly a brown dog leaped out of the brush. He jumped up on Henery, licking his face before Henery could push him away. A tall, thin Indian stepped from behind a tree.

Henery thought he knew this Indian. He was the boy Henery and Humility had met in the woods so many years before.

"Wasn't it you?" Henery asked the Indian. "Weren't you the one who had the sick dog?"

The Indian's serious face lit up, and he smiled. He offered his hand to Henery, white-man fashion. Henery smiled back as the two shook hands.

"Did the dog ever come back to you?" Henery asked. "This can't be the same dog!" He patted the dog's head.

"Dog come," said the Indian. "Me come for dog. Me whistle. Dog come. This not same dog. But good dog."

Henery saw that the Indian was friendly. Now the other Indians came out of the woods, one by one. They were all friendly.

"You made dog well. Now you make people well," said the Indian. "People sick—my people sick."

Meanwhile, back in the Winslow house, Mary was calm. She snuffed out the candles and made the children go up in the loft to hide.

John Winslow took charge. He placed Giles at a window. He himself stood behind the front door. Mary, holding a musket, guarded another window. Young Peregrine had gone to spread the alarm.

Everyone waited. There was no sound except a child's whisper and the crackling of a log in the fireplace.

Then there came a great banging on the door. It was loud and sudden in the silence.

A familiar voice shouted, "John, what's the matter with you people in there? Are you all in bed so early?"

"It's Henery!" Giles cried. He flung open the door.

Mary hurried to light the candles, and Henery faced the two armed men. Giles and John looked embarrassed.

"I've just brought a band of Indians to Governor Bradford's house," Henery explained. "They have had sickness and are in need of medicine. Also, their men have not been able to hunt. They need food. We must help."

"Of course," said everyone, even the children. They had crept down when they heard Henery's voice.

"They helped us," John said. "We're glad to help them."

Working, praying, sharing—so it would always be, as long as Plymouth stood.

Appendix

PRONOUNCING VOCABULARY*

KEY: ā as āte; ă as ădd; á as ásk; ä as fär; â as câre; ē as ēve; ĕ as ĕnd: ẽ as makẽr; ī as īce; ĭ as ĭll; ō as ōld; ô as fôr; ŏ as ŏdd; ōō as fōōd; ou as in town; ū as cūte; ŭ as ŭp; û as ûrn; zh as z in azure.

anchor (ăng'kẽr), a heavy piece of iron that holds a ship in one place in the water. The anchor is fastened to a chain which is attached to the ship. Sailors "drop anchor" when a ship reaches harbor.

Bartholomew (bär-thŏl'ô-mū), a boy's name. Bartholomew Allerton was one of the children who came over on the *May-flower*.

beaver (bē'vẽr), a small, gnawing animal which lives both on land and in water. Beaver fur is valuable.

Betty lamp (bĕt'ĭ lămp), an oil lamp with an open bowl for the oil and wick.

birch switch (bûrch swĭch), a birch twig, or a bundle of birch twigs tied together.

bleach (blēch), to take the color out of a piece of cloth or other material.

boat hook (bōt hŏŏk), a hook on a long pole. It is used in getting a boat in the right position in landing or pushing off.

bobbin (bŏb'ĭn), a small spool which holds thread.

Boston (bôs'tŭn), a city in Massachusetts, founded in 1630.

bound child (bound chīld), one of the children who were, in Pilgrim times, "bound out" for a certain number of years. The child's parents or guardian signed papers turning him over to a master, whom he had to serve. The master gave the child food, clothing, and a place to live.

brave (brāv), a young Indian warrior.

bunk (bŭngk), a bed on a ship. Bunks are fastened to the wall so that they will stay in place when the ship rolls.

Canonicus (ká-nŏn'ĭ-kŭs), a chief of the Narraganset Indians.

canopy bed (kăn'ô-pĭ bĕd) a four-poster bed with a rooflike covering. Curtains may hang down the sides and be pulled around the bed to shut out cold air.

Church of England (chûrch ŏv ĭng'glănd), the national church of England. In Pilgrim days

*The pronunciation system is used by permission. From Webster's *New International Dictionary*, Second Edition, copyright, 1934, 1939, 1945, by G. & C. Merriam Co.

English law said that all the people of England had to belong to this church and to worship in it.

cod (kŏd), a large fish, very important to New England trade. The cod was salted and could be kept for a long time.

colony (kŏl'ŏ-nĭ), a settlement in a new place. People who leave their own homes to make a new town or state are founding a colony.

common house (kŏm'ŭn hous), the first house the Pilgrims built. It was large enough that all the people could meet in it together.

compact (kŏm'păkt), an agreement. In signing the Mayflower Compact the Pilgrims agreed to make fair laws for their colony.

cooper (kōōp'ẽr), a barrelmaker. When barrels had to be made by hand, coopering was an important trade. Everything had to be shipped in great barrels, or hogsheads. The cooper prepared the barrel staves, or boards, hooped them, and made the barrels waterproof.

Corbitant (kôr'bĭ tänt), a chieftain of the Wampanoag Indians.

corselet (kôrs'lĕt), armor which covered the upper part of the body and looked somewhat like a sleeveless jacket.

Damaris (dăm'a-rĭs), a girl's name. Damaris Hopkins was Giles Hopkins' younger sister.

deacon (dē'kŭn), an officer or assistant in a church.

deck (dĕk), a floor of a ship. A small ship has only one deck. Larger ships may have several.

doublet (dŭb'lĕt), a close-fitting man's jacket or coat.

Ducksburrow (dŭks'bŭr-ō), the second town in the Plymouth colony, founded by the Pilgrims in 1632. The name was later changed to Duxbury.

dugout (dŭg'out), a simple kind of house built by digging a hole in the side of a hill or bluff and lining it with boards and clay. A pioneer family often lived in a dugout until a better house could be built.

elder (ĕl'dẽr), an officer of a church, or one whose age and experience give him special authority. The elder often led services when the church had no regular minister. Elder Brewster was the leader of the Pilgrim church for several years.

fire tongs (fīr tôngz), a pair of iron rods hinged together. Fire tongs are used to handle hot coals or logs in a fireplace.

flakes (flāks), in Pilgrim times, flat stones on which codfish were dried.

flax (flăks), a plant. Oil is produced from flaxseed and linen from the plant fibers.

flax brake (flăks brāk), a wooden frame with hinged jaws used in removing the woody part of flax from the fibers.

flax hackle (flăks hăk″l), a block of wood with wire teeth through which flax was combed.

flax swingle (flăks swĭng′g′l), a heavy wooden knife used to beat flax to remove the woody parts.

Fort Hill (fōrt hĭl), a hill behind the town of Plymouth. It was named Fort Hill because the Pilgrims made their fort and placed their cannon there.

forward deck (fôr′wĕrd dĕk), the front part of the main deck of a ship.

Giles (jīlz), a boy's name. Giles Hopkins was one of the children on the *Mayflower.*

gunpowder (gŭn′poudēr), an explosive powder used in guns. A Pilgrim had to pack musket balls and gunpowder into his musket through the muzzle end of the barrel.

hearth (härth), the bottom, or floor, of a fireplace.

hearth box (härth bŏks), a box used in cooking on shipboard. It contained sand on which a fire was built. A kettle was hung over the fire.

hemp (hĕmp), a plant grown for its fiber, which is used in making rope.

Henery (hĕn′ĕ rē), a boy's name, an old form of the name Henry. Henery Samson was one of the children of the *Mayflower.*

hogshead (hŏgz′hĕd), a very large barrel or barrel-shaped container.

hold (hōld), the part of a ship below the lower deck where cargo is carried.

hornbook (hôrn′bo͞ok), a flat piece of wood on which was mounted a sheet of paper with a thin sheet of horn to protect it. On the paper were the alphabet and the Lord's Prayer.

Humility (hŭ-mĭl′ĭ-tĭ), a girl's name. Humility Cooper was one of the children of the *Mayflower.*

Indian summer (ĭn′dĭ-ăn sŭm′ēr), a few days of warm weather in the late fall or early winter.

land ahoy (lănd à-hoi′), an expression used by sailors in hailing, welcoming, or announcing the sight of land.

landing party (lănd′ĭng pär′tĭ), a group of people who go ashore when a boat reaches land. They see what the land is like, make sure no enemies are about, and may get food, water, and fuel.

lean-to (lēn′to͞o), a shed with a one-slope roof. The shed may be built against a larger building or against trees.

lintel (lĭn′tĕl), the log or beam which forms the top of a fireplace.

178

longboat (lông′bōt), a long row-boat carried on a ship.

loom (lōōm), a frame used in weaving cloth.

mallard (măl′ērd), the wild duck.

Massasoit (măs′a-soit), a great chief of the Wampanoag tribe.

mast (màst), on a ship, a tall pole to which sails and rigging are fastened.

Master (màs′tēr), a form of address in Pilgrim days which was gradually changed to Mister. Only a gentleman was called Master.

mastiff (màs′tĭf), a large, powerful dog with a smooth coat and a big head.

meetinghouse (mēt′ĭng-hous), a church or other building used as a place for worshiping God.

Mistress (mĭs′trĕs), a form of address for ladies in Pilgrim times. This form has become Mrs.

Monhegan (mŏn-hē′găn), a small island off the coast of Maine.

musket (mŭs′kĕt), an old-fashioned gun which in Pilgrim times was fired by a matchlock or flintlock.

mutiny (mū′tĭ-nĭ), a rebellion of sailors or soldiers against authority. Mutiny is a very serious crime on a ship, where the captain's word is law.

Narraganset (năr a-găn′sĕt), a tribe of Indians who lived west of Narragansett Bay.

New England (nū ĭng′glănd), the northeastern part of the United States. Captain John Smith, in 1614, explored much of this territory and gave it the name of New England.

New World (nū wûrld), North and South America and the islands near them.

North Atlantic (nôrth ăt-lăn′tĭk), the northern part of the Atlantic Ocean. The North Atlantic is rough and stormy.

Oceanus (ō shē ăn′ŭs), a boy's name. Oceanus Hopkins was the first child born on the *Mayflower.*

Patuxet (păt ūks′ĕt), "Little Falls" or "Little Bay," the Indian name for the place that became New Plymouth.

pen (pĕn), an enclosure where animals or fowls are kept.

Pequot (pē′kwŏt), a tribe of Indians who occupied the territory that is now eastern Connecticut.

Pequot War (pē′kwŏt wôr), a war between the Pequot Indians and the white settlers, fought in 1637 and 1638.

Peregrine (pĕhr′ŭ grēn), a boy's name. Peregrine White was the second child born on the *Mayflower.*

pewter (pū′tēr), a substance much used in early times for plates, candlesticks, and other household ware. Pewter is made by mixing tin with some other metal, usually copper or lead.

pilgrim (pĭl'grĭm), a person who makes a journey, especially to a foreign land, for the sake of religion.

pillory (pĭl'ŏ-rĭ), a wooden frame which stood in a public place and was used for punishing people. The head and hands of a person being punished were thrust through holes in this frame and locked there.

Plymouth (plĭm'ŭth), England, a seaport on the southern coast of England.

Plymouth (plĭm'ŭth), Massachusetts, the Pilgrim settlement, built near the bay. It was often called New Plymouth. The territory had been named Plymouth first by Captain John Smith in 1614.

porringer (pŏr'ĭn-jēr), a small porridge dish or bowl, usually with a flat handle. The favorite material for porringers was pewter.

powwow (pou'wou), a meeting of the Indians for the purpose of performing certain ceremonies. A meeting of the Indians with white men was also given this name.

Puritan (pū'rĭ-tăn), one of the group who, in England, had wanted to purify the Church of England rather than separate from it.

quill pen (kwĭl pĕn), a pen made from a stiff feather. The pen was made by sharpening to a point the hollow end of the quill.

redskin (rĕd'skĭn), the white man's name for the American Indian. The brown skin of the Indian often has a reddish or coppery tinge.

reed (rēd), a tall grass which is dried and woven into baskets. North American Indians make beautiful baskets of reed.

rigging (rĭg'ĭng), the ropes and chains on a ship, needed for holding in place or for moving sails, masts, and other parts.

roper (rōp'ēr), one who makes rope.

runner (rŭn'ēr), in early days, one who carried messages by running. A runner had to be strong and fleet of foot.

Sabbath (săb'åth), the day of worship.

Salem (sā'lĕm), a town on the coast of Massachusetts, founded in 1626.

sassafras (săs'å-frăs), a group of trees of America. The root bark of one kind of sassafras is used as a medicine and for flavoring.

scribe (skrīb), a man who was the official writer for a group. In Pilgrim times many people could not write.

shovelboard (shŭv''l-bōrd), a game played in Pilgrim times. It was very much like our game of shuffleboard.

Sowams (sou'ahms), the village where Massasoit lived as chief of the Wampanoags.

spaniel (spăn'yĕl), a small or medium-sized dog with long, soft hair and large, floppy ears.

Speedwell (spēd'wĕl), the ship which carried some of the Pilgrims from Holland to England. Together with the *Mayflower*, this ship left England for the New World. But the *Speedwell* began to leak, and returned to England.

spinning wheel (spĭn'ĭng hwēl), a machine for making fibers into thread or yarn. The Pilgrims had both flax wheels and wheels for spinning woolen yarn.

spit (spĭt), an iron rod with a sharp point for holding a roast or fowl over the fire.

Squanto (skwän'tō), a Patuxet Indian who lived with the Pilgrims and taught them many useful skills.

squaw (skwô), the Algonquian word for an Indian woman.

stockade (stŏk-ād'), a fence made of tall, strong posts set close together. Stockades were often built around towns and forts as protection from enemies.

stocks (stŏks), a wooden frame used for punishing people. The person being punished sat with his feet, and often his hands, thrust through holes in the frame, which was locked.

thatch (thăch), a roof covering made of dried grasses or leaves.

tithingman (tĭth'ĭng-măn), a church officer in New England. It was the tithingman's duty to see that the Sabbath laws were obeyed and that order was kept at church.

tomahawk (tŏm'à-hôk), a small, light ax which was used by the Indians as a weapon.

treaty (trē'tĭ), a written agreement made between two or more groups of people.

trencher (trĕn'chĕr), a piece of tableware. Sometimes a trencher was made by hollowing out one side of a block of wood.

tripod kettle (trī'pŏd kĕt'l), a kettle which had three feet or legs so that it could be set in the hot coals of a fire.

venison (vĕn'ĭ-z'n), deer meat.

Virginia (vĕr-jĭn'ĭ-à), the territory where Jamestown, the first colony in North America, was founded in 1607.

Wampanoag (wŏm pà-nō'ăg), one of the Algonquian tribes of southern Massachusetts. Massasoit was chief of this tribe.

wampum (wŏm'pŭm), strands of shell beads. The Indians valued wampum greatly, using it both for ornaments and money.

water cress (wô'tĕr krĕs), a plant which grows wild in clear water. The leaves are used for salad.

181

whispering stick (hwĭs'pēr-ĭng stĭk), a stick of wood with a string fastened to each end. If a child whispered in school, the wood was placed between his teeth and the strings tied tightly around his head.

wick (wĭk), the twisted string or fibers in a candle or oil lamp. The wick is lighted and keeps drawing up tallow or oil for burning.

wigwam (wĭg'wôm), an Indian hut or tent. New England Indians made their wigwams by bending saplings into the shape of a hut and covering them with tree bark.

INDEX

Characters who appear throughout the story are listed here the first time they appear. Other characters are listed when some important information is given concerning them or when they come back into the story after having been gone for some time.

When a page number is given in bold type (135), it means that a picture of that object or person will be found on that page.

183